Glencoe McGraw-Hill

Chapter 13 Resource Masters

Geometry

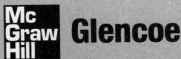
Mc Graw Hill Glencoe

CONSUMABLE WORKBOOKS Many of the worksheets contained in the Chapter Resource Masters booklets are available as consumable workbooks in both English and Spanish.

	ISBN10	ISBN13
Study Guide and Intervention Workbook	0-07-890848-5	978-0-07-890848-4
Homework Practice Workbook	0-07-890849-3	978-0-07-890849-1

Spanish Version

Homework Practice Workbook	0-07-890853-1	978-0-07-890853-8

ANSWERS FOR WORKBOOKS The answers for Chapter 13 of these workbooks can be found in the back of this Chapter Resource Masters booklet.

StudentWorks Plus™ This CD-ROM includes the entire Student Edition text along with the English workbooks listed above.

TeacherWorks Plus™ All of the materials found in this booklet are included for viewing, printing, and editing in this CD-ROM.

Spanish Assessment Masters (ISBN10: 0-07-890856-6, ISBN13: 978-0-07-890856-9) These masters contain a Spanish version of Chapter 13 Test Form 2A and Form 2C.

The McGraw·Hill Companies

 Glencoe

Send all inquiries to:
Glencoe/McGraw-Hill
8787 Orion Place
Columbus, OH 43240-4027

ISBN: 978-0-07-890522-3
MHID: 0-07-890522-2

Printed in the United States of America.

7 8 9 10 RHR 14 13

Contents

Teacher's Guide to Using the
Chapter 13 Resource Masters

The *Chapter 13 Resource Masters* includes the core materials needed for Chapter 13. These materials include worksheets, extensions, and assessment options. The answers for these pages appear at the back of this booklet.

All of the materials found in this booklet are included for viewing and printing on the *TeacherWorks Plus*™ CD-ROM.

Chapter Resources

Student-Built Glossary (pages 1–2) These masters are a student study tool that presents up to twenty of the key vocabulary terms from the chapter. Students are to record definitions and/or examples for each term. You may suggest that students highlight or star the terms with which they are not familiar. Give this to students before beginning Lesson 13-1. Encourage them to add these pages to their mathematics study notebooks. Remind them to complete the appropriate words as they study each lesson.

Anticipation Guide (pages 3–4) This master, presented in both English and Spanish, is a survey used before beginning the chapter to pinpoint what students may or may not know about the concepts in the chapter. Students will revisit this survey after they complete the chapter to see if their perceptions have changed.

Lesson Resources

Study Guide and Intervention These masters provide vocabulary, key concepts, additional worked-out examples and Check Your Progress exercises to use as a reteaching activity. It can also be used in conjunction with the Student Edition as an instructional tool for students who have been absent.

Skills Practice This master focuses more on the computational nature of the lesson. Use as an additional practice option or as homework for second-day teaching of the lesson.

Practice This master closely follows the types of problems found in the Exercises section of the Student Edition and includes word problems. Use as an additional practice option or as homework for second-day teaching of the lesson.

Word Problem Practice This master includes additional practice in solving word problems that apply the concepts of the lesson. Use as an additional practice or as homework for second-day teaching of the lesson.

Enrichment These activities may extend the concepts of the lesson, offer an historical or multicultural look at the concepts, or widen students' perspectives on the mathematics they are learning. They are written for use with all levels of students.

Graphing Calculator, TI-Nspire, or Spreadsheet Activities These activities present ways in which technology can be used with the concepts in some lessons of this chapter. Use as an alternative approach to some concepts or as an integral part of your lesson presentation.

Assessment Options

The assessment masters in the *Chapter 13 Resource Masters* offer a wide range of assessment tools for formative (monitoring) assessment and summative (final) assessment.

Student Recording Sheet This master corresponds with the standardized test practice at the end of the chapter.

Extended-Response Rubric This master provides information for teachers and students on how to assess performance on open-ended questions.

Quizzes Four free-response quizzes offer assessment at appropriate intervals in the chapter.

Mid-Chapter Test This 1-page test provides an option to assess the first half of the chapter. It parallels the timing of the Mid-Chapter Quiz in the Student Edition and includes both multiple-choice and free-response questions.

Vocabulary Test This test is suitable for all students. It includes a list of vocabulary words and 10 questions to assess students' knowledge of those words. This can also be used in conjunction with one of the leveled chapter tests.

Leveled Chapter Tests

- ***Form 1*** contains multiple-choice questions and is intended for use with approaching grade level students.
- ***Forms 2A and 2B*** contain multiple-choice questions aimed at on grade level students. These tests are similar in format to offer comparable testing situations.
- ***Forms 2C and 2D*** contain free-response questions aimed at on grade level students. These tests are similar in format to offer comparable testing situations.
- ***Form 3*** is a free-response test for use with beyond grade level students.

All of the above mentioned tests include a free-response Bonus question.

Extended-Response Test Performance assessment tasks are suitable for all students. Sample answers and a scoring rubric are included for evaluation.

Standardized Test Practice These three pages are cumulative in nature. It includes three parts: multiple-choice questions with bubble-in answer format, griddable questions with answer grids, and short-answer free-response questions.

Answers

- The answers for the Anticipation Guide and Lesson Resources are provided as reduced pages.
- Full-size answer keys are provided for the assessment masters.

13 Student-Built Glossary

This is an alphabetical list of the key vocabulary terms you will learn in Chapter 13. As you study the chapter, complete each term's definition or description. Remember to add the page number where you found the term. Add these pages to your Geometry Study Notebook to review vocabulary at the end of the chapter.

Vocabulary Term	Found on Page	Definition/Description/Example
circular permutation		
combination		
complement		
compound events		
conditional probability		
dependent events		
expected value		
factorial		
geometric probability		

(continued on the next page)

13 Student-Built Glossary (continued)

Vocabulary Term	Found on Page	Definition/Description/Example
independent events		
mutually exclusive		
permutation		
probability model		
probability tree		
random variable		
sample space		
simulation		
tree diagram		

2

Glencoe Geometry

13 Anticipation Guide

Probability and Measurement

Step 1   *Before you begin Chapter 1*

- Read each statement.
- Decide whether you Agree (A) or Disagree (D) with the statement.
- Write A or D in the first column OR if you are not sure whether you agree or disagree, write NS (Not Sure).

STEP 1 A, D, or NS	Statement	STEP 2 A or D
	1. A sample space can be represented using a tree diagram.	
	2. The Fundamental Counting Principle will find the number of possible outcomes of an event.	
	3. The number 0 factorial, or 0!, is equal to 0.	
	4. In a permutation, the order of the objects is not important.	
	5. When designing a simulation, always state any assumptions necessary.	
	6. The expected value of a random variable is the median value of a variable that one expects after repeating an experiment.	
	7. Two events are considered independent if the probability that one occurs does not affect the probability the other occurs.	
	8. Two events are considered mutually exclusive if they can happen at the same time and have similar outcomes.	

Step 2   *After you complete Chapter 13*

- Reread each statement and complete the last column by entering an A or a D.
- Did any of your opinions about the statements change from the first column?
- For those statements that you mark with a D, use a piece of paper to write an example of why you disagree.

13 Ejercicios Preparatorios

Probabilidad y medición

Antes de comenzar el Capítulo 13

- Lee cada enunciado.

- Decide si estás de acuerdo (A) o en desacuerdo (D) con el enunciado.

- Escribe A o D en la primera columna O si no estás seguro(a) de la respuesta, escribe NS (No estoy seguro(a)).

PASO 1 A, D o NS	Enunciado	PASO 2 A o D
	1. Un espacio muestral se puede representar usando un diagrama de árbol.	
	2. El número de resultados posibles de un evento se encuentra usando el principio fundamental de conteo.	
	3. El factorial del número 0, ó 0!, es igual a 0.	
	4. En una permutación, el orden de los objetos no es importante.	
	5. Al diseñar un simulacro, siempre se debe enunciar cualquier suposición necesaria.	
	6. El valor esperado de una variable aleatoria es el valor medio de la variable que uno espera después de repetir el experimento.	
	7. Dos eventos se consideran independientes si la probabilidad de que uno ocurra no afecta la probabilidad de que el otro ocurra.	
	8. Dos eventos se consideran mutuamente exclusivos si los eventos pueden ocurrir al mismo tiempo y tienen resultados semejantes.	

Después de completar el Capítulo 13

- Vuelve a leer cada enunciado y completa la última columna con una A o una D.

- ¿Cambió cualquiera de tus opiniones sobre los enunciados de la primera columna?

- En una hoja de papel aparte, escribe un ejemplo de por qué estás en desacuerdo con los enunciados que marcaste con una D.

13-1   Study Guide and Intervention

Representing Sample Spaces

Represent a Sample Space The **sample space** of an experiment is the set of all possible outcomes. A sample space can be found using an organized list, table, or tree diagram.

Example   Maurice packs suits, shirts, and ties that can be mixed and matched. Using the packing list at the right, draw a tree diagram to represent the sample space for business suit combinations.

> Maurice's Packing List
>
> 1. Suits: Gray, black, khaki
>
> 2. Shirts: White, light blue
>
> 3. Ties: Striped (But optional)

The sample space is the result of three stages:

- Suit color (G, B, or K)

- Shirt color (W or L)

- Tie (T or NT)

Draw a tree diagram with three stages.

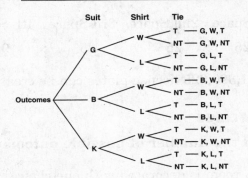

Exercises

Represent the sample space for each experiment by making an organized list, a table, and a tree diagram.

1. The baseball team can wear blue or white shirts with blue or white pants.

2. The dance club is going to see either *Sleeping Beauty* or *The Nutcracker* at either Symphony Hall or The Center for the Arts.

3. Mikey's baby sister can drink either apple juice or milk from a bottle or a toddler cup.

4. The first part of the test consisted of two true-or-false questions.

Lesson 13-1

13-1 Study Guide and Intervention (continued)

Representing Sample Spaces

Fundamental Counting Principle The number of all possible outcomes for an experiment can be found by multiplying the number of possible outcomes from each stage or event.

Example The pattern for a certain license plate is 3 letters followed by 3 numbers. The letter "O" is not used as any of the letters and the number "0" is not used as any of the numbers. Any other letter or number can be used multiple times. How many license plates can be created with this pattern?

Use the Fundamental Counting Principle.

1st Space		2nd Space		3rd Space		4th Space		5th Space		6th Space		Possible Outcomes
25	×	25	×	25	×	9	×	9	×	9	=	11,390,625

So 11,390,625 license plates can be created with this pattern.

Exercises

Find the number of possible outcomes for each situation.

1. A room is decorated with one choice from each category.

Bedroom Décor	Number of Choices
Paint color	8
Comforter set	6
Sheet set	8
Throw rug	5
Lamp	3
Wall hanging	5

2. A lunch at Lincoln High School contains one choice from each category.

Cafeteria Meal	Number of Choices
Main dish	3
Side dish	4
Vegetable	2
Salad	2
Salad Dressing	3
Dessert	2
Drink	3

3. In a catalog of outdoor patio plans, there are 4 types of stone, 3 types of edgers, 5 dining sets and 6 grills. Carl plans to order one item from each category.

4. The drama club held tryouts for 6 roles in a one-act play. Five people auditioned for lead female, 3 for lead male, 8 for the best friend, 4 for the mom, 2 for the dad, and 3 for the crazy aunt.

13-1 Skills Practice

Representing Sample Spaces

Represent the sample space for each experiment by making an organized list, a table, and a tree diagram.

1. Michelle could take a summer job in California or Arizona at a hotel or a bed-and-breakfast.

2. Jeremy could go to baseball or soccer camp as a counselor or an assistant director.

3. Brad could buy his mom a $25 or $50 gift card for a spa or a housecleaning service.

Find the number of possible outcomes for each situation.

4. Marie's family is buying a house. They must choose one from each category.

House Plans	Number of Choices
Subdivision location	4
Floor plans	5
Garage size	2
Front yard landscape package	3
Backyard pool package	3

5. Mr. Thomson is choosing his cable TV. He must choose one from each category.

Cable TV Plans	Number of Choices
Channel packages	16
DVR system	3
Contract length	3
Service contract	2
Include phone	2
Include Internet	2

6. Valentine gift sets come with a choice of 4 different teddy bears, 8 types of candy, 5 balloon designs, and 3 colors of roses.

7. Joni wears a school uniform that consists of a skirt or pants, a white shirt, a blue jacket or sweater, white socks and black shoes. She has 3 pairs of pants, 3 skirts, 6 shirts, 2 jackets, 2 sweaters, 6 pairs of socks and 3 pairs of black shoes.

13-1   Practice

Representing Sample Spaces

Represent the sample space for each experiment by making an organized list, a table, and a tree diagram.

1. Tavya can spend the summer with her cousins or her grandparents at the lake or at the beach.

2. Jordan can write his final essay in class or at home on a scientific or an historical topic.

3. Julio can join the Air Force or the Army before or after college.

Find the number of possible outcomes for each situation.

4. Josh is making a stuffed animal.

Animal Options	Number of Choices
Animals	10
Type of stuffing	3
Sound effect	5
Eye color	3
Outfit	20

5. Kelley is buying an ice cream cone. Assume one of each category is ordered.

Ice Cream	Number of Choices
Type of cone	3
Flavors	20
Cookie toppings	4
Candy toppings	8

6. Movie-themed gift baskets come with a choice of one of each of the following: 4 flavors of popcorn, 4 different DVDs, 4 types of drinks, and 8 different kinds of candy.

7. **INTERNSHIP** Jack is choosing an internship program that could take place in 3 different months, in 4 different departments of 3 different firms. Jack is only available to complete his internship in July. How many different outcomes are there for Jack's internship?

13-1 Word Problem Practice

Representing Sample Spaces

1. **SCHOOL SUPPLIES** Eva is shopping for school supplies. She has a choice of one of each of the following: 6 backpacks, 8 notebooks, 3 pencil cases, 3 brands of pencils, 8 brands of pens, 4 types of calculator, and 4 colors of highlighter. How many different choices does she have for school supplies?

2. **LAPTOPS** Chloe is buying a laptop. She has a choice of 3 hard drive sizes, 3 processor speeds, 4 colors, 2 screen sizes, 2 warranty options, and 4 cases. She knows she wants a blue laptop with the longest warranty. How many choices does she have for laptops?

3. **BOARD GAMES** Below is a spinner used in a board game. If the spinner is spun 4 times, how many different possible outcomes are there?

4. **BASKETBALL** In the NBA there must be a minimum of 14 players on a team's roster. A team has the minimum number of players where 3 are centers, 4 are power forwards, 2 are small forwards, 3 are shooting guards, and the rest are point guards. For this situation, how many different possible outcomes are there?

   Source: *NBA Players Association*

5. **VACATION RENTAL** A brochure describes available vacation rentals in Colorado and Florida. In Colorado you can choose a 1 or 2 week stay in a 1- or 2-bedroom suite. In Florida you can choose a 1, 2 or 3 week stay in a 2- or 3-bedroom suite, along the beach or not.

   a. How many outcomes are available in Colorado?

   b. How many outcomes are available in Florida?

   c. How many total outcomes are available?

Lesson 13-1

13-1 Enrichment

Traveling Salesman Problem

A traveling salesperson plans to sell a product in several different cities. The salesperson wants to find the shortest route to visit each city, and then return to the starting point. How does the salesperson find the shortest distance to travel to each city?

This problem, called the Traveling Salesman Problem, might seem simple, but in fact finding efficient solutions have proven to be very difficult. To date, computers running through the entire **solution space** or **sample space**, of the problem, have arrived at a solution. The computer looks at all possible combinations of cities to visit, computes each combination's length, then finds the shortest distance. Even with the help of computers, however, is not clear if the most efficient general solution has been found.

Example Find the number of ways a person can visit 5 different cities and then return to the first city.

If a person starts at one city there are 4 other cities to visit. Then there are 3 cities and after that 2 cities and then one city. After that they must return to the original city. So:

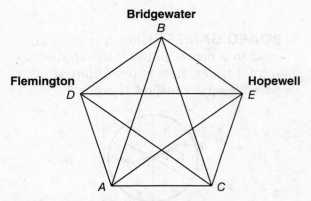

First		Second		Third		Fourth	
4	·	3	·	2	·	1	= 24

There are 24 different ways to visit 5 cities.

Exercises

Find the sample space of visiting each of the n cities and returning to the first city.

1. $n = 7$ **2.** $n = 3$ **3.** $n = 8$

4. $n = 11$ **5.** $n = 12$ **6.** $n = 4$

13-2 Study Guide and Intervention

Probability with Permutations and Combinations

Probability Using Permutations

A **permutation** is an arrangement of objects where order is important. To find the number of permutations of a group of objects, use the **factorial**. A factorial is written using a number and !. The following are permutation formulas:

$$n! = n \cdot (n-1) \cdot (n-2) \cdot \ldots \cdot 2 \cdot 1$$

$$5! = 5 \cdot 4 \cdot 3 \cdot 2 \cdot 1 = 120$$

n distinct objects taken r at a time	$_nP_r = \dfrac{n!}{(n-r)!}$
n objects, where one object is repeated r_1 times, another is repeated r_2 times, and so on	$\dfrac{n!}{r_1! \cdot r_2! \cdot \ldots \cdot r_k!}$
n objects arranged in a circle with no fixed reference point	$\dfrac{n!}{n}$ or $(n-1)!$

Example The cheer squad is made up of 12 girls. A captain and a co-captain are selected at random. What is the probability that Chantel and Cadence are chosen as leaders?

Find the number of possible outcomes.

$$_{12}P_2 = \frac{12!}{(12-2)!} = \frac{12!}{10!} = 12 \cdot 11 = 132$$

Find the number of favorable outcomes.

$$2! = 2$$

The probability of Chantel and Cadence being chosen is

$$\frac{\text{favorable outcomes}}{\text{total number of outcomes}} = \frac{2}{132} = \frac{1}{66}$$

Exercises

1. **BOOKS** You have a textbook for each of the following subjects: Spanish, English, Chemistry, Geometry, History, and Psychology. If you choose 4 of these at random to arrange on a shelf, what is the probability that the Geometry textbook will be first from the left and the Chemistry textbook will be second from the left?

2. **CLUBS** The Service Club is choosing members at random to attend one of four conferences in LA, Atlanta, Chicago, and New York. There are 20 members in the club. What is the probability that Lana, Sherry, Miguel, and Jerome are chosen for these trips?

3. **TELEPHONE NUMBERS** What is the probability that a 7-digit telephone number generated using the digits 2, 3, 2, 5, 2, 7, and 3 is the number 222-3357?

4. **DINING OUT** A group of 4 girls and 4 boys is randomly seated at a round table. What is the probability that the arrangement is boy-girl-boy-girl?

13-2 Study Guide and Intervention (continued)

Probability with Permutations and Combinations

Probability Using Combinations A **combination** is an arrangement of objects where order is NOT important. To find the number of combinations of n distinct objects taken r at a time, denoted by $_nC_r$, use the formula:

$$_nC_r = \frac{n!}{(n-r)!\,r!}$$

Example Taryn has 15 soccer trophies but she only has room to display 9 of them. If she chooses them at random, what is the probability that each of the trophies from the school invitational from the 1st through 9th grades will be chosen?

Step 1 Since the order does not matter, the number of possible outcomes is

$$_{15}C_9 = \frac{15!}{(15-9)!\,(9!)} = 5005$$

Step 2 There is only one favorable outcome—the 9 specific trophies being chosen.

Step 3 The probability that these 9 trophies are chosen is

$$\frac{\text{number of favorable outcomes}}{\text{total number of outcomes}} = \frac{1}{5005}.$$

Exercises

1. **ICE CREAM** Kali has a choice of 20 flavors for her triple scoop cone. If she chooses the flavors at random, what is the probability that the 3 flavors she chooses will be vanilla, chocolate, and strawberry?

2. **PETS** Dani has a dog walking business serving 9 dogs. If she chooses 4 of the dogs at random to take an extra trip to the dog park, what is the probability that Fifi, Gordy, Spike and Fluffy are chosen?

3. **CRITIQUE** A restaurant critic has 10 new restaurants to try. If he tries half of them this week, what is the probability that he will choose The Fish Shack, Carly's Place, Chez Henri, Casa de Jorge, and Grillarious?

4. **CHARITY** Emily is giving away part of her international doll collection to charity. She has 20 dolls, each from a different country. If she selects 10 of them at random, what is the probability she chooses the ones from Ecuador, Paraguay, Chile, France, Spain, Sweden, Switzerland, Germany, Greece, and Italy?

5. **ROLLER COASTERS** An amusement park has 12 roller coasters. Four are on the west side of the park, 4 are on the east side, and 4 are centrally located. The park's Maintenance Department randomly chooses 4 roller coasters for upgrades each month. What is the probability that all 4 roller coasters on the west side are chosen in March?

13-2 Skills Practice

Probabilities With Permutations and Combinations

1. **DISPLAY** The Art Club is displaying the students' works in the main hallway. In a row of 12 randomly ordered paintings, what is the probability that Tim's and Abby's paintings are in the 6th and 7th positions?

2. **LINE UP** When the 18 French class students randomly line up for a fire drill, what is the probability that Amy is first and Zach is last in line?

3. **TRY-OUTS** Ten students made call-backs for the three lead roles in the school play. What is the probability Sarah, Maria, and Jimenez will be chosen for the leads?

4. **SECURITY** Parking stickers contain randomly generated numbers with 5-digits ranging from 1 to 9. No digits are repeated. What is the probability that a randomly generated number is 54321?

5. **MEETING** Micah is arranging 15 chairs in a circle for an ice breaker game for the first club meeting. If people choose their seats randomly, what is the probability Micah sits in the seat closest to the door?

6. **MERRY-GO-ROUND** The mall has a merry-go-round with 12 horses on the outside ring. If 12 people randomly choose those horses, what is the probability they are seated in alphabetical order?

7. **PROMOTION** Tony is promoting his band's first concert. He contacts 10 local radio stations. If 4 of them agree to interview him on the air, what is the probability they are the top 4 stations in the area?

8. **TALENT SHOW** The Sign Language Club is choosing 10 of its 15 members to perform at the school talent show. What is the probability that the 10 people chosen are the 10 seniors in the club?

Lesson 13-2

13-2   Practice

Probability with Permutations and Combinations

1. FORMAL DINING You are handed 5 pieces of silverware for the formal setting shown. If you guess their placement at random, what is the probability that the knife and spoon are placed correctly?

2. GOLF The standings list after the first day of a 3-day tournament is shown below. What is the probability that Wyatt, Gabe, and Isaac will all finish in the top 3?

DAY 1 STANDINGS	
MCAFEE, DAVID	−3
FORD, GABE	−2
STANDISH, TRISTAN	−2
NICHOLS, WYATT	−1
PURCELL, JACK	−1
ANDERSON, BILL	−1
WRIGHT, ISAAC	−1
FILBERT, MITCH	+1

3. PHONE NUMBER What is the probability that a phone number generated using the digits 1, 2, 2, 4, 5, 5, 6, and 2 is the number 654-5222?

4. LETTERS Jaclyn bought some decorative letters for a scrapbook project. If she selected a permutation of the letters shown, what is the probability that they would form the word "photography"?

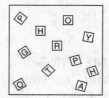

5. COFFEE BREAK A group of 6 friends of varying ages meets at a coffee shop and sits in a circle. What is the probability that the youngest member of the group sits in the seat closest to the door?

6. JEWELRY Bonita bought her mom a charm bracelet. Each charm is labeled with a one-word message. What is the probability that the 5 charms were hung in the order: dream, believe, love, laugh, inspire?

7. COLLEGES Mark wants to visit the 10 colleges he is considering attending. He can only spend the night at 3 of them. What is the probability that he spends a night at Rutgers University, a night at the University of Miami, and a night at Clemson University?

8. ODD JOBS Matthew put fliers advertising his lawn service on the doors of 20 families' houses in his neighborhood. If 6 families called him, what is the probability that they were the Thompsons, the Rodriguezes, the Jacksons, the Williamses, the Kryceks, and the Carpenters?

13-2 Word Problem Practice

Probability with Permutations and Combinations

1. RANDOM NUMBERS A random number generator is a computer program that produces random numbers. What is the probability that it will produce a number less than 1,000 for a 5-digit number? (Hint: 00125 = 125)

2. SCHEDULE At Randolph High School, there are 17 different classes offered to sophomores each semester. Four classes can be taken each semester and students may not repeat a class during the year. What is the probability of the student taking English, History I, Algebra and Spanish II the first semester and taking History II, Spanish III, Geometry and Biology the next semester?

3. UNITED NATIONS The UN Security Council has 5 permanent members and 10 non-permanent members. Italy is one of 192 UN member states and is not a permanent member of the Security Council. What is the probability that Italy is on the Security Council?

4. CARDS What is the probability in a line of these 5 cards that the ace would be first from the left and the king would be second from the left?

5. GEOMETRY Points A, B, C, D, and E are coplanar but no 3 are collinear.

a. What is the total number of lines that can be determined by these points?

b. What is the probability that $\overleftrightarrow{AB}$ would be chosen at random from all of the possible lines formed?

Lesson 13-2

13-2 Enrichment

Finding Combinations Using Pascal's Triangle

Blaise Pascal (June 19, 1623 – August 19, 1662) was a French mathematician, philosopher, and physicist. One of his contributions to mathematics is the geometric arrangement of binomial coefficients called Pascal's Triangle. The triangle is constructed in rows by adding terms from previous rows. The first row contains a single digit 1 and is referred to as "Row 0." The outside of the triangle is formed of 1's in a diagonal.

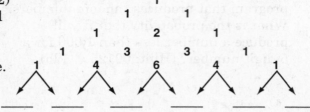

Look at the blank row shown in the diagram. Add the entries from the previous row to find the entries for this row. The next row would then be: 1, 5 (*because 1 + 4 = 5*), 10 (*because 4 + 6 = 10*), 10 (*because 6 + 4 = 10*), 5 (*because 4 + 1 = 5*), and 1. Write these values in the spaces provided.

One use of the values in Pascal's Triangle is finding the number of items taken in combination. For example, the value of $_5C_2$ is found in row 5, entry 2. Remembering that each row begins with entry 0 (which is always equal to 1), The entry found in row 5, entry 2 is 10, $_5C_2 = 10$.

Exercises

Use Pascal's Triangle above to answer the following.

1. Complete the next three rows of Pascal's Triangle.

      1   5   10   10   5   1

2. Use Pascal's Triangle to find $_7C_3$.

3. What do you notice about the values of $_7C_1$ and $_7C_6$?

4. How many 3-topping pizzas can be made from a choice of 8 toppings?

5. What is the probability that the pizza made in Exercise 4 is a pepperoni, sausage, and onion pizza?

6. What is the probability that out of Char's 6 closest friends, Ava and Jenna plan a surprise party for her?

13-3 Study Guide and Intervention

Geometric Probability

Probability with Length Probability that involves a geometric measure is called **geometric probability**. One type of measure is length.

Look at line segment $\overline{KL}$.

If a point, M, is chosen at random on the line segment, then

$P(M \text{ is on } \overline{KL}) = \dfrac{KL}{RS}$.

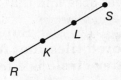

Example Point X is chosen at random on $\overline{AD}$. Find the probability that X is on $\overline{AB}$.

$P(X \text{ is on } \overline{AB}) = \dfrac{AB}{AD}$ Length probability ratio

$= \dfrac{8}{16}$ $AB = 8$ and $AD = 8 + 2 + 6 = 16$

$= \dfrac{1}{2}$, 0.5, or 50%   Simplify.

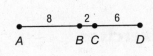

Exercises

Point M is chosen at random on $\overline{ZP}$. Find the probability of each event.

1. $P(M \text{ is on } \overline{ZQ})$

2. $P(M \text{ is on } \overline{QR})$

3. $P(M \text{ is on } \overline{RP})$

4. $P(M \text{ is on } \overline{QP})$

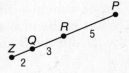

5. **TRAFFIC LIGHT** In a 5-minute traffic cycle, a traffic light is green for 2 minutes 27 seconds, yellow for 6 seconds, and red for 2 minutes 27 seconds. What is the probability that when you get to the light it is green?

6. **GASOLINE** Your mom's mini van has a 24 gallon tank. What is the probability that, when the engine is turned on, the needle on the gas gauge is pointing between $\dfrac{1}{4}$ and $\dfrac{1}{2}$ full?

Lesson 13-3

13-3 Study Guide and Intervention *(continued)*

Geometric Probability

Probability with Area Geometric probabilities can also involve area. When determining geometric probability with targets, assume that the object lands within the target area and that it is equally likely that the object will land anywhere in the region.

Example Suppose a coin is flipped into a reflection pond designed with colored tiles that form 3 concentric circles on the bottom. The diameter of the center circle is 4 feet and the circles are spaced 2 feet apart. What is the probability the coin lands in the center?

P(coin lands in center) $= \dfrac{\text{area of center circle}}{\text{area of base of pond}}$

$= \dfrac{4\pi}{36\pi}$

$= \dfrac{1}{9}$, about 0.11, or 11%

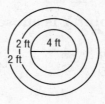

Exercises

1. **LANDING** A parachutist needs to land in the center of a target on a rectangular field that is 120 yards by 30 yards. The target is a circular design with a 10 yard radius. What is the probability the parachutist lands somewhere in the target?

2. **CLOCKS** Jonus watches the second hand on an analog clock as it moves past the numbers. What is the probability that at any given time the second hand on a clock is between the 2- and the 3-hour numbers?

Find the probability that a point chosen at random lies in the shaded region.

3.

4.

5.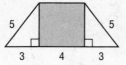

Use the spinner to find each probability. If the spinner lands on a line it is spun again.

6. P(pointer landing on red)

7. P(pointer landing on blue)

8. P(pointer landing on green)

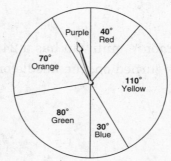

13-3 Skills Practice

Geometric Probability

Point X is chosen at random on $\overline{LP}$. Find the probability of each event.

1. $P(X$ is on $\overline{LN})$ _____

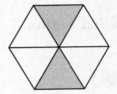

2. $P(X$ is on $\overline{MO})$

Find the probability that a point chosen at random lies in the shaded region.

3.

4.

5.

6. **DESKWORK** The diagram shows the top of a student's desk at home. A dart is dropped on the desk. What is the probability the dart lands on the book report?

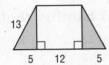

7. **FROGS** Three frogs are sitting on a 15-foot log. The first two are spaced 5 feet apart and the third frog is 10 feet away from the second one. What is the probability that when a fourth frog hops onto the log it lands between the first two?

8. **RADIO CONTEST** A radio station is running a contest in which listeners call in when they hear a certain song. The song is 2 minutes 40 seconds long. The radio station promised to play it sometime between noon and 4 P.M. If you tune in to that radio station during that time period, what is the probability the song is playing?

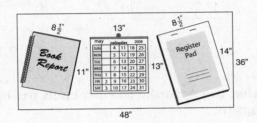

Use the spinner to find each probability. If the spinner lands on a line it is spun again.

9. P(pointer landing on yellow)

10. P(pointer landing on orange)

Lesson 13-3

13-3 Practice

Geometric Probability

Point L is chosen at random on $\overline{RS}$. Find the probability of each event.

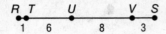

1. $P(L$ is on $\overline{TV})$

2. $P(L$ is on $\overline{US})$

Find the probability that a point chosen at random lies in the shaded region.

3.
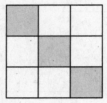

4.

5.

Use the spinner to find each probability. If the spinner lands on a line it is spun again.

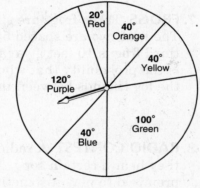

6. P(pointer landing on purple)

7. P(pointer landing on red)

8. **PIGS** Four pigs are lined up at the feeding trough as shown in the picture. What is the probability that when a fifth pig comes to eat it lines up between the second and third pig?

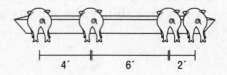

9. **MUSIC** A certain company plays Mozart's *Eine Kleine Nachtmusik* when its customers are on hold on the telephone. If the length of the complete recording is 2 hours long, what is the probability a customer put on hold will hear the Allegro movement which is 6 minutes, 31 seconds long?

13-3 Word Problem Practice

Geometric Probability

1. **DARTS** A dart is thrown at the dartboard shown. Each sector has the same central angle. The dart has equal probability of hitting any point on the dartboard. What is the probability that the dart will land in a shaded sector?

2. **SPINNERS** Jamie, Joe, and Pat celebrate the end of each work week by ordering spring rolls from a Chinese restaurant. The order comes with 4 spring rolls so somebody gets an extra roll. Because Jamie works full time and Joe and Pat work half time, they decide who gets the extra roll by using a spinner that has a 50% chance of coming up Jamie, and 25% chances of coming up either Joe or Pat. Design such a spinner.

3. **RAIN** A container has a square top with a hole as shown. What is the probability that a raindrop that hits the container falls into the hole? Round your answer to the nearest thousandth.

7 in.   14 in.

4. **ELECTRON MICROSCOPES** Crystal places a 7 millimeter by 10 millimeter rectangular plate into the sample chamber of an electron microscope. A black and white checkerboard pattern of 1-millimeter squares was painted over the plate to identify different treatments of the material. When she turns on the monitor, she has no idea at what point on the plate she is looking because the white and black contrast does not show up on the screen. If there are 2 more black squares than white squares, what is the probability that she is looking at a white square?

5. **ENTERTAINMENT** A rectangular dance stage is lit by two lights that light up circular regions of the stage. The circles have radii of the same length and each circle passes through the center of the other. The stage perfectly circumscribes the two circles. A spectator throws a bouquet of flowers onto the stage. Assume the bouquet has an equal chance of landing anywhere on the stage. (*Hint:* Use inscribed equilateral triangles.)

a. What is the probability that the flowers land on a lit part of the stage?

b. What is the probability that the flowers land on the part of the stage where the spotlights overlap?

Lesson 13-3

13-3 Enrichment

Polygon Probability

Each problem on this page involves one or more regular polygons. To find the probability of a point chosen at random being in the shaded region, you need to find the ratio of the shaded area to the total area. If you wish, you may substitute numbers for the variables.

Find the probability that a point chosen at random in each figure is in the shaded region. Assume polygons that appear to be regular are regular. Round your answer to the nearest hundredth.

1.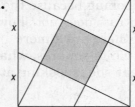

2.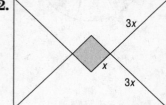

3.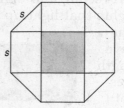

4.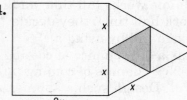

5.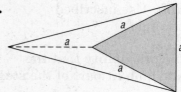

6.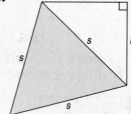

13-3 Spreadsheet Activity

Geometric Probability

You can use a spreadsheet to determine geometric probability.

Example   Use a spreadsheet to find the probability
of a parachutist landing in the center of this landing pad
made up concentric circles.

Step 1   Enter the value of the radius of the center circle in cell
A1 and the value of the radius of the whole circle in cell B1.

Step 2   In cell C1 enter an equals sign followed by 3.14*(A1^2).
Then press enter. In cell D1 Enter an equals sign followed by
3.14*(B1^2). Then press enter.

Step 3   In cell E1 enter an equals sign followed
by C1/D1. Then press Enter. This is the
geometric probability of a parachutist
landing in the center of the concentric
circles.

The diagram shows concentric circles labeled "2 yd   2 yd   2 yd".

Spreadsheet "Geoprob3":

	A	B	C	D	E
1	2	6	12.57	113.1	0.11
2					

Sheet 1 / Sheet 2 / Sheet 3

The probability of a parachutist landing in the center of the landing pad is 0.11.

Exercises

Use a spreadsheet to find the probability of each situation.

1. Refer to Example 1. Find the probability if the radius of the center circle is 4 yards.

2. What is the probability that an object thrown into the backyard
will land in the pool?

The diagram shows a pool (60 ft wide, with 80 ft and 40 ft dimensions) inside a 100 ft yard.

3. Refer to Exercise 2. Suppose the size of the yard remained
the same, but the pool was circular with a diameter of 40 feet.
What is the new probability that an object thrown into the
backyard will land in the pool?

4. Find the probability of a care package dropped from
an airplane landing on the warehouse in this field.

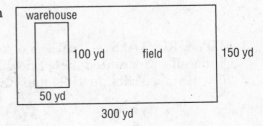

The diagram shows a warehouse (50 yd, 100 yd) inside a field (300 yd, 150 yd).

5. Refer to Exercise 3. Find the probability the
care package lands somewhere in the field rather
than on the warehouse.

Lesson 13-3

13-4 Study Guide and Intervention

Simulations

Design a Simulation
A **probability model** is a mathematical model that matches something that happens randomly. A **simulation** is a way to use the model to recreate a situation to help determine the situation's probability.

To design a simulation:
1. Determine each possible outcome and its theoretical probability.
2. State any assumptions.
3. Describe an appropriate probability model for the situation.
4. Define a trial for the situation and state the number of trials to be conducted.

Example Joni got on base 40% of her times at bat last season. Design a simulation to determine the probability that she will get on base in her next at bat this season.

The possible outcomes are Joni gets on base (40%) and Joni doesn't get on base (60%). Assume that Joni will have 90 at bats this season.

Use a spinner divided into two sectors, one containing 40% of the spinner's area, or a central angle of 144°, and the other 60%, or 216°. A trial, one spin of the spinner, will represent one at bat. A successful trial will be getting on base and a failed trial will be not getting on base. The simulation will contain 90 trials.

Exercises

Design a simulation using a geometric probability model.

1. **WRESTLING** Carlos is the star of the wrestling team. Carlos pinned 80% of his opponents in wrestling matches last season.

2. **JEANS** A trendy jeans store sells jeans in 4 different styles. Last year 45% of their sales was straight leg jeans, 30% was boot cut jeans, 15% was low rise jeans, and 10% was easy fit.

3. **MOVIE RENTALS** A local video store has 5 videos in its fairytale section. Last month Cinderella was rented 35%, Snow White was rented 30%, Sleeping Beauty was rented 20%, Rumpelstiltskin 10%, and Rapunzel 5%.

13-4 Study Guide and Intervention (continued)

Simulations

Summarize Data from a Simulation After a simulation is created, the results must be reported with numerical and graphical displays of the data. Compare theoretical and experimental probabilities or expected and average values depending on the type of simulation you run.

Example In a carnival game, a ball is rolled up an incline toward circular regions with different point values. The center circle has a diameter of 6 inches and each successive circle has a radius 4 inches greater than the previous circle.

Let the random variable X represent the point value assigned to a region on the game. The expected value $E(X)$ is found by adding the products of each region's point value and the geometric probability of landing in that region.

$$E(X) = 100 \cdot \frac{72}{121} + 200 \cdot \frac{40}{121} + 300 \cdot \frac{9}{121} \approx 148$$

The frequency table shows the result of the simulation after using a graphing calculator to generate 50 trials. Use these numbers to construct a bar graph and to calculate average value.

Outcome	Frequency
Region 100	19
Region 200	16
Region 300	15
Total	50

$$\text{Average value} = 100 \cdot \frac{19}{50} + 200 \cdot \frac{16}{50} + 300 \cdot \frac{15}{50} = 192$$

The average value is higher than the expected value.

Exercises

1. **BASEBALL** For a particular baseball player, out of the total number of times he reaches base he gets a walk 6% of the time, a single 55% of the time, a double 30% of the time, a triple 1% of the time, and a home run 8% of the time. The frequency table shows the results of a simulation. Construct a bar graph and compare the experimental probabilities with the theoretical probabilities.

Outcome	Frequency
Walk	5
Single	60
Double	25
Triple	0
Home run	10
Total	100

2. **CARNIVAL** In a game similar to the game in the above Example, there are four regions in which the ball can fall. The probability that Jani can get 100 points in a roll is 25%, the probability of 200 points is 50%, of 300 points is 20%, and of 400 points is 5%. Calculate the expected value for each roll.

Lesson 13-4

13-4 Skills Practice

Simulations

Design and conduct a simulation using a geometric probability model. Then report the results using appropriate numerical and graphical summaries.

1. **INTERNET** Cory has an online store and auction site. Last year he sold 85% of his inventory.

2. **CANDY** Haley works at a candy store. There are 10 types of bulk candy. Find the probability that one type of candy will be chosen more than once in 10 trials.

Design and conduct a simulation using a random number generator. Then report the results using appropriate numerical and graphical summaries.

3. **FOOD** According to a survey by a restaurateur's magazine on favorite types of food, 45% of their readers chose Italian, 25% Mexican, 15% American, 10% French, and 5% Ethnic.

13-4 Practice

Simulations

Design and conduct a simulation using a geometric probability model. Then report the results using appropriate numerical and graphical summaries.

1. **TRACK** Sean successfully handed off his baton 95% of the time in the 4 × 4 relay last season.

2. **BOARD GAME** A game has 50 cards with 10 each numbered 1 to 5, and a player must draw a 2 or a 3 to move out of the "start" position.

Design and conduct a simulation using a random number generator. Then report the results using appropriate numerical and graphical summaries.

3. **REAL ESTATE** A real estate company reviewed last year's purchases to determine trends in sizes of homes purchased. The results are shown in the table.

Homes	Purchase %
2BR	10%
3BR	35%
4BR	30%
5BR	15%
6BR	10%

4. **GRADES** On Jonah's math quizzes last semester he scored an A 80% of the time, a B 15% of the time, and a C 5% of the time.

Lesson 13-4

13-4 Word Problem Practice

Simulations

1. SIMULATIONS Marta designed a simulation using a coin and a spinner with six equal sections. What situation could Marta have been given to design this simulation?

2. WEATHER Isaiah says he can use a coin for his simulation of whether or not it will rain tomorrow because there are only 2 possible outcomes. Manny says the weather forecaster said there is a 70% chance it will rain, so a coin is not a good model. Who is correct? Why?

3. TRAVEL According to a survey done by a travel agency, 40% of their cruise clients went to the Bahamas, 25% to Mexico, 20% to Alaska, and 15% to Greece. When Jeremy and Jayme were asked to design a simulation that could be used to estimate the probability of a client going to each of these places, Jeremy designed the spinner below.

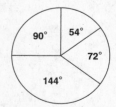

Jayme wants to assign integers to each destination and use the random number generator on her graphing calculator. Which model would allow more trials conducted in a shorter period of time?

4. GOLF The local driving range advertises that more than 50% of their clients will hit a ball longer than 250 yards at their range. George designed a simulation and then observed for a day at the range. His results are displayed in the histogram below.

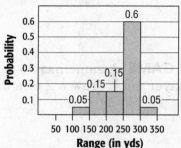

Is the driving range's statement correct?

5. CARNIVAL A ring toss game awards different point values depending on which dowels rings land. The diagram shows the point values for the different dowels. For this experiment, assume each tossed ring will land on a dowel.

```
   25  25  25  25  25
   ⊙   ⊙   ⊙   ⊙   ⊙
      50  50  50
25⊙ ⊙   ⊙   ⊙  ⊙25
      50 100  50
25⊙ ⊙   ⊙   ⊙  ⊙25
      50  50  50
25⊙ ⊙   ⊙   ⊙  ⊙25
   ⊙   ⊙   ⊙   ⊙   ⊙
   25  25  25  25
```

a. Tommy and Catherine calculated the expected value for this experiment as $E(Y) = 36$. Are they correct?

b. When Tommy and Catherine conducted the simulation with 50 trials, they found an estimated value of 37.5. Is this reasonable? Why or why not?

13-4 Enrichment

Pseudorandom Numbers

A random number generator produces numbers with unpredictable outcomes. The random numbers cannot be reproduced using the same generator. A pseudorandom number generator produces numbers that have properties similar to a set of random numbers. While the numbers are not random, they appear to be random. A pseudorandom number generator is used in such applications as MP3 players and computer software. When *random* is chosen on an MP3 player, the generator pseudorandomly chooses a song number. While it may seem that the order of the songs is random, sometimes you may notice a pattern in the song choices. For this reason, the numbers generated are not truly random numbers.

Suppose you have downloaded music onto your MP3 player. You have 6 favorite artists and 10 songs from each of those artists are in your play list. When it is playing in random mode, your MP3 player is programmed to choose the artist and then the song.

1. Design a simulation using a geometric probability model that would find the probability of any of the 60 songs playing (you may have to use more than one device).

2. Conduct the simulation you designed in Exercise 1.

3. Report the results of the simulation.

Suppose you have only 3 favorite artists, but you have 5 songs from Artist 1, 10 songs from Artist 2, and 15 songs from Artist 3. Design and conduct a simulation using a random number generator to answer the following questions.

4. What is the probability a song by Artist 2 will play?

5. What is the probability a song by Artist 3 will play?

6. Do you expect a song from Artist 3 to be more or less likely to play than a song by Artist 1? Why?

Lesson 13-4

13-4 Graphing Calculator Activity

Probability Simulation: Conducting a Simulation

Example 1 Use Probability Simulation to simulate choosing a card from a deck of 52 cards.

Step 1 Choose the Probability Simulation Function from the Applications menu. Press ENTER.

- Choose **5. Draw Cards**

- Choose **Draw** from the menu at the bottom of the screen and have the calculator randomly draw cards. A table appears at the right to keep track of the cards drawn.

Step 2 Repeat until 10 cards have been drawn.

Example 2 Design and conduct a simulation using a random number generator.

The school library reviewed the books checked out last month. The results are as follows: 40% fiction, 30% non fiction, 20% biographies, and 10% other.

Step 1 Assign the numbers 1 to 10 to accurately represent the probability data: $1 - 4$ = fiction; $5 - 7$ = non fiction; $8 - 9$ = biographies; 10 = other.

Step 2 Use the calculator. Choose the Probability Simulation Function from the Applications menu. Press ENTER.

- Choose **6. Random Numbers**

- Choose **SET** from the menu at the bottom of the screen. Set the calculator to choose 5 numbers, in the range from $1 - 10$, allowing repeats. Press GRAPH to choose **OK**.

Step 3 Choose **DRAW**. The calculator will randomly choose 5 numbers and record them in the table. Repeat this 5 times.

Exercises

Design a simulation using the given method. Then use the calculator to conduct the simulation.

Simon made 50% of the goals he attempted in soccer last year.

1. toss coins

2. roll dice

3. pick marbles

4. spin spinner

13-5 Study Guide and Intervention

Probabilities of Independent and Dependent Events

Independent and Dependent Events **Compound events**, or two or more simple events happening together, can be independent or dependant. Events are **independent events** if the probability of one event does not affect the probability of the other. Events are **dependent events** if one event in some way changes the probability that the other occurs. The following are the **Multiplication Rules for Probability**.

Probability of Two Independent Events	$P(A \text{ and } B) = P(A) \cdot P(B)$
Probability of Two Dependent Events	$P(A \text{ and } B) = P(A) \cdot P(B|A)$

$P(B|A)$ is the **conditional probability** and is read *the probability that event B occurs given that event A has already occurred.*

Example The P.E. teacher puts 10 red and 8 blue marbles in a bag. If a student draws a red marble, the student plays basketball. If a student draws a blue marble, the student practices long jump. Suppose Josh draws a marble, and not liking the outcome, he puts it back and draws a second time. What is the probability that on each draw his marble is blue?

Let B represent a blue marble.

$P(B \text{ and } B) = P(B) \cdot P(B)$ Probability of independent events

$\qquad = \dfrac{4}{9} \cdot \dfrac{4}{9} \text{ or } \dfrac{16}{81}$ $P(B) = \dfrac{4}{9}$

So, the probability of Josh drawing two blue marbles is $\dfrac{16}{81}$ or about 20%.

Exercises

Determine whether the events are *independent* or *dependent*. Then find the probability.

1. A king is drawn from a deck of 52 cards, then a coin is tossed and lands heads up.

2. A spinner with 4 equally spaced sections numbered 1 through 4 is spun and lands on 1, then a die is tossed and rolls a 1.

3. A red marble is drawn from a bag of 2 blue and 5 red marbles and not replaced, then a second red marble is drawn.

4. A red marble is drawn from a bag of 2 blue and 5 red marbles and then replaced, then a red marble is drawn again.

Lesson 13-5

13-5 Study Guide and Intervention (continued)

Probabilities of Independent and Dependent Events

Conditional Probabilities Conditional probability is used to find the probability of dependent events. It also can be used when additional information is known about an event.

The conditional probability of B given A is $P(B|A) = \dfrac{P(A \text{ and } B)}{P(A)}$

where $P(A) \neq 0$.

Example The Spanish Club is having a Cinco de Mayo fiesta. The 10 students randomly draw cards numbered with consecutive integers from 1 to 10. Students who draw odd numbers will bring main dishes. Students who draw even numbers will bring desserts. If Cynthia is bringing a dessert, what is the probability that she drew the number 10?

Since Cynthia is bringing dessert, she must have drawn an even number.

Let A be the event that an even number is drawn.

Let B be the event that the number 10 is drawn.

$P(B|A) = \dfrac{P(A \text{ and } B)}{P(A)}$ Conditional Probability

$\qquad = \dfrac{0.5 \cdot 0.1}{0.5}$ $P(A) = \frac{1}{2} = 0.5$ and $P(B) = \frac{1}{10} = 0.1$

$\qquad = 0.1$ Simplify.

The probability Cynthia drew the number 10 is 0.1 or 10%.

Exercises

1. A blue marble is selected at random from a bag of 3 red and 9 blue marbles and not replaced. What is the probability that a second marble selected will be blue?

2. A die is rolled. If the number rolled is less than 5, what is the probability that it is the number 2?

3. A quadrilateral has a perimeter of 16 and all side lengths are even integers. What is the probability that the quadrilateral is a square?

4. A spinner with 8 evenly sized sections and numbered 1 through 8 is spun. Find the probability that the number spun is 6 given that it is an even number.

13-5   Skills Practice

Probabilities of Independent and Dependent Events

Determine whether the events are *independent* or *dependent*. Then find the probability.

1. In a game two dice are tossed and both roll a six.

2. From a standard deck of 52 cards, a king is drawn without replacement. Then a second king is drawn.

3. From a drawer of 8 blue socks and 6 black socks, a blue sock is drawn and not replaced. Then another blue sock is drawn.

Find each probability.

4. A green marble is selected at random from a bag of 4 yellow, 3 green, and 9 blue marbles and not replaced. What is the probability a second marble selected will be green?

5. A die is tossed. If the number rolled is between 2 and 5, inclusive, what is the probability the number rolled is 4?

6. A spinner with the 7 colors of the rainbow is spun. Find the probability that the color spun is blue, given the color is one of the three primary colors.

7. **VENDING** Mina wants to buy a drink from a vending machine. In her pocket are 2 nickels, 3 quarters and 5 dimes. What is the probability she first pulls out a quarter and then another quarter?

8. **ESSAYS** Jeremy's English class is drawing randomly for people to critique their essays. Jeremy draws first and his friend, Brandon, draws second. If there are 20 people in their class, what is the probability they will draw each other's names?

Lesson 13-5

13-5 Practice

Probabilities of Independent and Dependent Events

Determine whether the events are *independent* or *dependent*. Then find the probability.

1. From a bag of 5 red and 6 green marbles, a red marble is drawn and not replaced. Then a green marble is drawn.

2. In a game, you roll an odd number on a die and then spin a spinner with 6 evenly sized spaces numbered 1 to 6 and get an even number.

3. A card is randomly chosen from a standard deck of 52 cards then replaced, and a second card is then chosen. What is the probability that the first card is the ace of hearts and the second card is the ace of diamonds?

Find each probability.

4. A die is tossed. If the number rolled is greater than 2, what is the probability that the number rolled is 3?

5. A black shoe is selected at random from a bin of 6 black shoes and 4 brown shoes and not replaced. What is the probability that a second shoe selected will be black?

6. A spinner with 12 evenly sized sections and numbered 1 to 12 is spun. What is the probability that the number spun is 12 given that the number is even?

7. **GAME** In a game, a spinner with 8 equally sized sections numbered 1 to 8 is spun and a die is tossed. What is the probability of landing on an odd number on the spinner and rolling an even number on the die?

8. **APPROVAL** A survey found that 8 out of 10 parents approved of the new principal's performance. If 4 parents' names are chosen, with replacement, what is the probability they all approve of the principal's performance?

13-5   Word Problem Practice

Probabilities of Independent and Dependent Events

1. **DRIVING** The probability that a person has received a speeding ticket is 0.35. The probability of a person driving a red car is 0.15. What is the probability of randomly choosing a driver with a speeding ticket whose car is not red?

2. **GAMES** In a game, the spinner with 4 spaces numbered 1 to 4 is spun and a die is rolled.

   What is the probability of spinning an even number on the spinner and rolling an even number on the die?

3. **CARDS** Three cards are drawn and not replaced from a standard deck. What is the probability that all three cards will be from different suits?

4. **HEALTH** Jane conducted a survey at her school and found that the probability of a student contracting a version of the flu last year at her school was 5% She also found the probability of a student contracting the stomach flu at her school last year was 1%. What is the probability that if a person develops the flu, it will be the stomach flu?

5. **BIRTHDAYS** Since there are 365 days in a year, the probability of a person's birthday on any random day is about 0.00274.

APRIL 2008						
Sunday	Monday	Tuesday	Wednesday	Thursday	Friday	Saturday
		1	2	3	4	5
6	7	8	9	10	11	12
13	14	15	16	17	18	19
20	21	22	23	24	25	26
27	28	29	30			

   a. What is the probability that two people will have the same birthday?

   b. What is the probability that out of thirty people, two will have the same birthday?

Lesson 13-5

13-5 Enrichment

Weather Forecasting

When you watch the news the weather person might say, "there will be a 60% chance of rain tomorrow." This means that $P(\text{rain tomorrow}) = \frac{60}{100}$. Notice that this also says that $P(\text{no rain tomorrow}) = \frac{40}{100}$. But rain tomorrow is dependent upon a number of factors; such as if it rains today, if clouds form over the night, or if it rained today in a city to the east.

Day	Conditions	High/Low
Monday	Sunny	70/50
Tuesday	Rain	68/54
Wednesday	Partly Cloudy	62/53

Weather forecasts are predictions of what might happen; they are not always correct. They are independent of the weather because their forecast has no effect on the weather.

Example A forecaster for the Springfield Times says there is a 40% chance that it will rain. The forecaster is correct 75% of the time.

a. What is the probability the forecaster will be right and it will rain?

Since these events are independent the probability will be $\frac{40}{100} \cdot \frac{75}{100} = \frac{3000}{10,000}$ or $\frac{3}{10}$.

b. What is the probability that the forecaster will be wrong and it not rain?

The probability that the forecaster will be wrong is 25%, while the probability that it will not rain is 60%. Since these events are independent the probability will be $\frac{25}{100} \cdot \frac{60}{100} = \frac{1500}{10,000}$ or $\frac{15}{100}$.

Exercises

A forecaster for the Union Herald says that there is a 40% chance that clouds will form. They also say that if clouds form there is a 60% chance of rain. If the forecaster is correct 55% of the time, find the following probabilities.

1. clouds will form and it will not rain

2. clouds will not form and the forecaster will be right

3. clouds will not form and the forecaster will be wrong

4. clouds will form, it will rain and the forecaster will be right

5. clouds will form, it will rain and the forecaster will be wrong

13-6 Study Guide and Intervention

Probabilities of Mutually Exclusive Events

Mutually Exclusive Events If two events cannot happen at the same time, and therefore have no common outcomes, they are said to be **mutually exclusive**. The following are the **Addition Rules for Probability**:

Probability of Mutually Exclusive Events	$P(A \text{ or } B) = P(A) + P(B)$
Probability of Non-Mutually Exclusive Events	$P(A \text{ or } B) = P(A) + P(B) - P(A \text{ and } B)$

Example   At the ballpark souvenir shop, there are 15 posters of the first baseman, 20 of the pitcher, 14 of the center fielder, and 12 of the shortstop. What is the probability that a fan choosing a poster at random will choose a poster of the center fielder or the shortstop?

These are mutually exclusive events because the posters are of two different players.

Let C represent selecting a poster of the center fielder.

Let S represent selecting a poster of the shortstop.

$$P(C \text{ or } S) = P(C) + P(S)$$
$$= \frac{14}{61} + \frac{12}{61}$$
$$= \frac{26}{61} \text{ or about } 43\%$$

Exercises

Determine whether the events are *mutually exclusive* or *not mutually exclusive*. Then find the probability. Round to the nearest hundredth.

1. **SHELTER** selecting a cat or dog at the animal shelter that has 15 cats, 25 dogs, 9 rabbits and 3 horses

2. **GAME** rolling a 6 or an even number on a die while playing a game

3. **AWARDS** The student of the month gets to choose his or her award from 9 gift certificates to area restaurants, 8 CDs, 6 DVDs, or 5 gift cards to the mall. What is the probability that the student of the month chooses a CD or DVD?

4. **STUDENT COUNCIL** According to the table shown at the right, what is the probability that a person on a student council committee is a junior or on the service committee?

Committee	Soph.	Junior	Senior
Service	4	5	6
Advertising	3	2	2
Dances	4	8	6
Administrative Liaison	1	1	4

13-6 Study Guide and Intervention (continued)

Probabilities of Mutually Exclusive Events

Probabilities of Complements The complement of an event A is all of the outcomes in the sample space that are not included as outcomes of event A.

Probability of the Complement of an Event	$P(\text{not } A) = 1 - P(A)$

Example A school has a photography display of 100 pictures. One of the pictures will be chosen for display at the district office. Lorenzo has 3 pictures on display. What is the probability that one of his photographs is not chosen?

Let A represent selecting one of Lorenzo's photographs.

Then find the probability of the complement of A.

$P(\text{not } A) = 1 - P(A)$ Probability of a complement

$\qquad = 1 - \dfrac{3}{100}$ Substitution

$\qquad = \dfrac{97}{100}$ or 0.97 Simplify

The probability that one of Lorenzo's photos is not selected is 97%.

Exercises

Determine the probability of each event.

1. If there is a 4 in 5 chance that your mom will tell you to clean your room today after school, what is the probability that she won't?

2. What is the probability of drawing a card from a standard deck and not getting a spade?

3. What is the probability of flipping a coin and not landing on tails?

4. What is the probability of rolling a pair of dice and not rolling a 6?

5. A survey found that about 90% of the junior class is right handed. If 2 juniors are chosen at random out of 100 juniors, what is the probability that at least one of them is not right handed?

13-6 Skills Practice

Probabilities of Mutually Exclusive Events

Determine whether the events are *mutually exclusive* or *not mutually exclusive*. Then find the probability. Round to the nearest tenth of a percent if necessary.

1. drawing a card from a standard deck and choosing a king or an ace

2. rolling a pair of dice and doubles or a sum of 6 is rolled

3. drawing a two or a heart from a standard deck of 52 cards

4. rolling a pair of dice and a sum of 8 or 12 is rolled

Determine the probability of each event.

5. If the chance of being selected for the student bailiff program is 1 in 200, what is the probability of not being chosen?

6. If you have a 40% chance of making a free throw, what is the probability of missing a free throw?

7. What is the probability of spinning a spinner numbered 1 to 6 and not landing on 5?

8. Jeanie bought 10 raffle tickets. If 250 were sold, what is the probability that one of Jeanie's tickets will not be selected?

13-6 Practice

Probabilities of Mutually Exclusive Events

Determine whether the events are *mutually exclusive* or *not mutually exclusive*. Then find the probability. Round to the nearest hundredth.

1. drawing a card from a standard deck and choosing a 7 or a 10

2. rolling a pair of dice and getting a sum of either 6 or 8

3. selecting a number from a list of integers 1 to 20 and getting a prime or even number

4. drawing a card from a standard deck and getting a queen or a heart

Determine the probability of each event. Round to the nearest hundredth.

5. What is the probability of drawing a card from a standard deck and not choosing an ace?

6. What is the probability of rolling a pair of dice and not rolling the same number?

7. If the chance of being chosen for the principal's task force is 3 in 20, what is the probability of not being chosen?

8. What is the probability of spinning a spinner numbered from 1 to 12 and not landing on 6?

9. **TRAFFIC** If the chance of making a green light at a certain intersection is 35%, what is the probability of arriving when the light is yellow or red?

10. **RAFFLE** Michael bought 50 raffle tickets. If 1000 were sold, what is the probability that one of Michael's tickets will not win?

13-6 Word Problem Practice

Probabilities of Mutually Exclusive Events

1. **CHESS** A chess board has 64 squares, 32 white and 32 black, and is played with 16 black and 16 white pieces.

If all the pieces are placed randomly on the board, what is the probability of two white knights being on black squares or a black bishop being on a black square?

2. **PARKS** The table below shows the Parks and Recreation Department classes and the number of participants aged 7–9.

Age	Swimming	Drama	Art
7	40	35	25
8	30	21	14
9	20	44	11

What is the probability that a participant chosen at random is in Drama or is an 8-year-old?

3. **CARDS** What is the probability of pulling two cards from a 52-card deck that are both red or both fours?

4. **COLLEGE** In Evan's senior class of 100 students, 89% are attending in-state colleges. If two people are chosen at random from the entire class, what is the probability that at least one of them is not going to an in-state college?

5. **DESIGN** Dennis and Kelly are designing a game for a third grade math class to help students practice their basic facts. They decide that the game will use a pair of dice and the players will have to find the sum of the numbers rolled. Dennis and Kelly created the table below to help determine probabilities.

1, 1	1, 2	1, 3	1, 4	1, 5	1, 6
2, 1	2, 2	2, 3	2, 4	2, 5	2, 6
3, 1	3, 2	3, 3	3, 4	3, 5	3, 6
4, 1	4, 2	4, 3	4, 4	4, 5	4, 6
5, 1	5, 2	5, 3	5, 4	5, 5	5, 6
6, 1	6, 2	6, 3	6, 4	6, 5	6, 6

Each player will roll the pair of dice twice during that player's turn.

a. What is the probability of rolling a pair or two numbers that add to seven?

b. What is the probability of rolling two numbers that add to an even number or not rolling a 2?

13-6 Enrichment

Demographics

Demographics is the term used to refer to characteristics of the population including age, race, gender, education level, income, employment status, and other variables. Marketing research used by advertisers and polling data used by politicians are two areas in which demographics are an important part of the data. Sometimes the people under consideration fall into more than one category. Sometimes the events being researched are mutually exclusive.

Suppose an exit poll held outside a voting area on the day of an election produced these results. Use the table to answer the questions below.

Age and Gender	Votes for Candidate A	Votes for Candidate B
18–30 Male	19	32
18–30 Female	31	18
31–45 Male	51	12
31–45 Female	43	20
46–60 Male	42	35
46–60 Female	20	42
60+ Male	45	21
60+ Female	27	18

1. Which events are mutually exclusive?

2. Find the probability that a 46–60 year-old male would vote for Candidate A.

3. Find the probability that a female would vote for Candidate A.

4. Find the probability that someone who voted for Candidate B was female and age 18–30.

5. According to the data, on which demographic(s) does Candidate A need to focus campaign efforts?

6. On which demographic(s) does Candidate B need to focus campaign efforts?

42

13 Student Recording Sheet

Use this recording sheet with pages 954–955 of the Student Edition.

Assessment

Multiple Choice

Read each question. Then fill in the correct answer.

1. Ⓐ Ⓑ Ⓒ Ⓓ   3. Ⓐ Ⓑ Ⓒ Ⓓ   5. Ⓐ Ⓑ Ⓒ Ⓓ

2. Ⓕ Ⓖ Ⓗ Ⓙ   4. Ⓕ Ⓖ Ⓗ Ⓙ   6. Ⓕ Ⓖ Ⓗ Ⓙ

Short Response/Gridded Response

Record your answer in the blank.

For gridded response questions, also enter your answer in the grid by writing each number or symbol in a box. Then fill in the corresponding circle for that number or symbol.

7. _____ (grid in)

8. _____

9. _____ (grid in)

10. _____ (grid in)

11. _____

12. _____

7.

9.

10.

Extended Response

Record your answers for Question 13 on the back of this paper.

13 Rubric for Scoring Extended-Response

General Scoring Guidelines

- If a student gives only a correct numerical answer to a problem but does not show how he or she arrived at the answer, the student will be awarded only 1 credit. All extended-response questions require the student to show work.

- A fully correct answer for a multiple-part question requires correct responses for all parts of the question. For example, if a question has three parts, the correct response to one or two parts of the question that required work to be shown is *not* considered a fully correct response.

- Students who use trial and error to solve a problem must show their method. Merely showing that the answer checks or is correct is not considered a complete response for full credit.

Exercise 13 Rubric

Score	Specific Criteria
4	Students demonstrate their understanding of independent and dependent events in probability by providing correct probabilities supported by well thought out, complete explanations.
3	A generally correct solution, but may contain minor flaws in reasoning or computation.
2	A partially correct interpretation and/or solution to the problem.
1	A correct solution with no supporting evidence or explanation.
0	An incorrect solution indicating no mathematical understanding of the concept or task, or no solution is given.

13 **Chapter 13 Quiz 1**

(Lessons 13-1 and 13-2)

1. Sam is deciding between majoring in history or journalism at Eastern State or Central State. Write an organized list to represent the sample space.

1. _____

2. The service club is going to build a house for a needy family or serve dinner at a homeless shelter over spring break or Memorial Day weekend. Draw a tree diagram to represent the sample space.

2. _____

3. Find the number of possible outcomes for an election of class officers in which there are 2 candidates for president, 3 for vice president, 4 for secretary and 3 for treasurer.

3. _____

4. The Art Club is randomly choosing a president and vice president from its 15 members. What is the probability that Matt and Lisa are chosen?

4. _____

5. What is the probability that a phone number generated with digits 0, 1, 2, 2, 3, 3, and 5 is 323-0125 if the first two digits cannot be a 0 or 1?

5. _____

13 **Chapter 13 Quiz 1**

(Lesson 13-3)

1. Point E is chosen at random on $\overline{XY}$. Find the probability that E is on $\overline{AB}$.

```
    2      3        4
 •——•——————•——————•
 X  A      B      Y
```

1. _____

2. A city bus stops at the city park every 15 minutes. What is the probability that someone arriving at a random time would have to wait more than 5 minutes?

85° orange, 50° red, 95° yellow, 100° purple, 30° green

2. _____

3. Find the probability of the pointer of the spinner at the rigt lands on purple.

3. _____

For Questions 4 and 5, find the probability of a point chosen at random being in the shaded area.

4.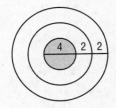

4. _____

5.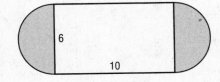

5. _____

13   Chapter 13 Quiz 3

(Lessons 13-4 and 13-5)

SCORE _____

1. Describe a spinner that could be used to simulate an event with 2 possible outcomes, one with a probability of 60%.

1. _____

2. How should numbers be assigned to use a random number generator for the following situation?

    Probability choosing blue: 40%
    Probability choosing green: 20%
    Probability choosing red: 30%
    Probability choosing purple: 10%

2. _____

3. A coin is tossed and a die is rolled. Find the probability of tossing heads and a rolling a 6.

3. _____

4. A card is drawn from a standard deck of 52 cards and then replaced. Find the probability of drawing a king and then an ace.

4. _____

5. A card is drawn from a standard deck of 52 cards and not replaced. Find the probability of drawing a king and then an ace.

5. _____

- -

13   Chapter 13 Quiz 4

(Lesson 13-6)

SCORE _____

1. A card is drawn from a standard deck. Find the probability the card drawn is a king or an ace.

1. _____

2. Two dice are rolled. Find the probability that the sum is 9 or doubles are rolled.

2. _____

3. Two dice are rolled. Find the probability that the sum is 12 or doubles are rolled.

3. _____

4. If the chance of rain is 80%, what is the probability that it will not rain?

4. _____

5. Dana bought 50 raffle tickets. If 300 were sold, what is the probability that Dana does not win the raffle?

5. _____

13   Chapter 13 Mid-Chapter Test

(Lessons 13-1 through 13-3)

SCORE _____

Part I   *Write the letter for the correct answer in the blank at the right of each question.*

1. Tossing a coin is an example of :

   A an outcome   **C** an event
   B a two-stage experiment   **D** a multi-stage experiment

   1. _____

2. At Jeans R Us, pairs of jeans comes in 9 different brands, 5 different cuts, and 4 colors. How many different types of jeans are there?
   F 18   **G** 120   **H** 180   **J** 954

   2. _____

3. For her graduation party, Lisa can invite 5 of her 15 classmates to go to a water park. What is the probability that, chosen at random, Jenny, Amy, Liza, Katy, and Emily are invited?

   A $\dfrac{1}{360,360}$ **B** $\dfrac{5}{360,360}$ **C** $\dfrac{5}{3003}$ **D** $\dfrac{1}{3003}$

   3. _____

4. Point X is chosen at random on $\overline{AB}$.
   Find P (X is on $\overline{AD}$).

   F $\dfrac{1}{3}$ **H** $\dfrac{1}{2}$
   G $\dfrac{1}{9}$ **J** $\dfrac{1}{6}$

   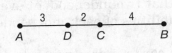

   4. _____

5. Use the spinner at the right. Find the probability the pointer lands on purple.

   A 0.375   **C** 0.135
   B 0.25   **D** 0.10

   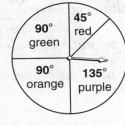

   5. _____

Part II

6. Mitchell is planning to travel to either Europe or South America either the summer after his junior year or after his senior year. Represent the sample space with an organized list.

   6. _____

7. Draw a tree diagram to represent the sample space from the event in Question 6.

8. A teacher randomly assigns her 30 students 4-digit I.D. numbers using the digits 0 to 9. No digits are repeated within an ID number. What is the probability one of the ID numbers is 9876?

   7. _____

9. Kayla and Bianca each bought one raffle ticket at the school fair. If 50 tickets were sold, what is the probability Kayla bought ticket number 7 and Bianca bought ticket number 10?

   8. _____

10. If you randomly selected a permutation of the letters E, O, G, M, E, R, T, Y, what is the probability they would spell "geometry"?

   9. _____

   10. _____

Assessment

13 Chapter 13 Vocabulary Test

SCORE _____

circular permutation	factorial	probability model
combination	Fundamental Counting	probability tree
complement	Principle	random variable
compound events	geometric probability	sample space
conditional probability	independent events	simulation
dependent events	mutually exclusive events	tree diagram
expected value	permutation	

Write whether each sentence is *true* or *false*. If false, replace the underlined word or phrase to make a true sentence.

1. The events of rolling a die and tossing a coin are considered <u>compound events</u>.

    1. _____

2. A coin is tossed twice. The <u>sample space</u> is TT, TH, HT, and HH.

    2. _____

3. The probability that two independent events both occur is the <u>sum</u> of the probabilities of each independent event.

    3. _____

4. When choosing a card randomly from a deck of cards, choosing a 5 or a spade are not considered <u>mutually exclusive</u> events.

    4. _____

Choose the correct term to complete the sentence.

5. An event is one or more outcomes of a(n) (*experiment, sample space*).

    5. _____

6. The (*permutation, factorial*) of a positive integer is the product of the integers less than or equal to that integer.

    6. _____

Choose from the terms above to complete each sentence.

7. A(n) _____ is a mathematical model used to match a random phenomenon.

    7. _____

8. Suppose a sock is randomly drawn from a dresser drawer and not replaced. The another sock is chosen. These two events are considered to be _____.

    8. _____

Define each term in your own words.

9. tree diagram

    9. _____

10. Fundamental Counting Principle

    10. _____

13   Chapter 13 Test, Form 1

Write the letter for the correct answer in the blank at the right of each question.

1. If a coin is tossed twice, how many possible outcomes are there?

    A 0   **B** 1   **C** 2   **D** 4

1. _____

2. Use the Fundamental Counting Principle to find the number of possible outcomes if a die is rolled 4 times.

    F 14!   **G** 6!   **H** 1296   **J** 24

2. _____

3. Find the number of possible outcomes for creating an outfit from 4 pairs of pants, 3 shirts, and 5 pairs of shoes.

    A 12   **B** 60   **C** 4!   **D** 3!

3. _____

4. The 5 starting members of the basketball team are lining up for a picture. What is the probability they are lined up shortest to tallest?

    F $\frac{1}{120}$ **G** 1.2   **H** $\frac{1}{60}$ **J** 5!

4. _____

5. The hostess sat your group of 6 at a round table. If you all choose your seats randomly, what is the probability you sit closest to the kitchen?

    A $\frac{1}{6}$ **B** $\frac{1}{720}$ **C** $\frac{6}{720}$ **D** $\frac{1}{120}$

5. _____

6. What is the probability that a randomly selected permutation of the letters A, A, B, C, S, U would spell "abacus"?

    F $\frac{1}{720}$ **G** $\frac{1}{360}$ **H** $\frac{1}{180}$ **J** $\frac{1}{90}$

6. _____

7. Point X is chosen at random on $\overline{JM}$. Find $P(X$ is on $\overline{KM})$.

    A 0.29   **C** 0.47

    B 0.4   **D** 0.79

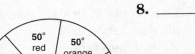

7. _____

8. Your computer checks for new email messages every 15 minutes. If you sit down at your computer at a random time, what is the probability you will have to wait more than 5 minutes for the computer to check for new email messages?

    F $\frac{1}{3}$ **G** $\frac{2}{3}$ **H** $\frac{5}{15}$ **J** $\frac{1}{15}$

8. _____

9. Use the spinner shown. Find the probability the pointer lands on blue.

    A $\frac{1}{3}$ **C** $\frac{30}{180}$

    B $\frac{1}{12}$ **D** $\frac{1}{6}$

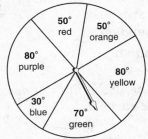

9. _____

10. Amy made 40% of her free throws last year. Which of the following best describes a simulation that could be used to find the probability of whether or not Amy makes her next free throw?

    F tossing a coin 40 times   **H** a dart board with 2 equal sections

    G a spinner with a 144° sector   **J** a bag of 40 marbles

10. _____

Assessment

13   Chapter 13 Test, Form 1 *(continued)*

11. Which of the following best describes an appropriate graphic
representation of data from a simulation?

   A frequency table   **C** bar graph

   B line graph   **D** pictograph   **11.** _____

12. The Law of Large Numbers says that the more trials of a simulation
you conduct, the difference between the average and expected values:

   F decreases   **H** remains the same

   G increases   **J** approaches infinity   **12.** _____

13. Find the probability of a point chosen at
random being in the shaded area of the
diagram at the right.

   A $\frac{4}{9}$ **C** $\frac{1}{4}$

   B $\frac{1}{9}$ **D** $\frac{1}{2}$ **13.** _____

14. The object of a popular carnival game is to roll a ball up an incline
into regions with different values. The probability that Angus will get
100 points in a roll is 30%, 200 points is 55%, and 300 points is 15%.
The expected value, $E(X)$, of a roll is:

   F 100   **G** 185   **H** 200   **J** 275   **14.** _____

15. A card is drawn from a standard deck and not replaced. Then a
second card is drawn. What is the probability that both cards are
aces?

   A $\frac{3}{676}$ **B** $\frac{4}{663}$ **C** $\frac{7}{2652}$ **D** $\frac{1}{221}$ **15.** _____

16. Jonus rolls a die two times. What is the probability that he rolls an
even number and then an odd number?

   F $\frac{1}{4}$ **G** $\frac{2}{3}$ **H** $\frac{1}{6}$ **J** $\frac{1}{2}$ **16.** _____

17. The events of drawing an ace or a spade from a standard deck of
playing cards are:

   A independent   **C** mutually exclusive

   B dependent   **D** not mutually exclusive   **17.** _____

18. What is the probability of *not* drawing a diamond from a standard
deck of 52 cards?

   F $\frac{1}{13}$ **G** $\frac{3}{4}$ **H** $\frac{13}{52}$ **J** $\frac{1}{4}$ **18.** _____

Bonus The hostess sat your group of 6 family members at a round table.
      If you all choose you seats randomly, what is the probability you
      sit on your mom's right?   **B:** _____

SCORE _____

13 Chapter 13 Test, Form 2A

Write the letter for the correct answer in the blank at the right of each question.

1. If a coin is tossed twice, three of the possible outcomes are HH, HT, and TH. What is the missing outcome?

   A TH   **B** TT   **C** HT   **D** TH

   1. _____

2. A die is rolled 4 times. Using the Fundamental Counting Principle, which will find the number of possible outcomes?

   F $4 \times 3 \times 2 \times 1$ **H** 6×4

   G $6 \times 5 \times 4 \times 3$ **J** $6 \times 6 \times 6 \times 6$

   2. _____

3. Find the number of possible outcomes for creating an outfit from 2 pairs of pants, 2 skirts, 3 shirts, and 5 pairs of shoes.

   A 12   **B** 60   **C** 4!   **D** $2 \times 2!$

   3. _____

4. The 5 starting members of the field hockey team are lining up for a picture. What is the probability the Jane will stand in the center of the picture and her best friend will be on her right?

   F 120   **G** $\frac{1}{120}$ **H** $\frac{1}{20}$ **J** $\frac{1}{60}$

   4. _____

5. For your birthday dinner, you and your family sit at a round table. If the 6 members of your family all choose your seats randomly, what is the probability you are sitting in age order?

   A $\frac{1}{6}$ **B** $\frac{1}{720}$ **C** $\frac{1}{120}$ **D** $\frac{6}{120}$

   5. _____

6. What is the probability that a randomly selected permutation of the letters G, G, I, W, L, E would spell "wiggle"?

   F $\frac{1}{720}$ **G** $\frac{1}{360}$ **H** $\frac{1}{180}$ **J** $\frac{1}{90}$

   6. _____

7. Ten people serve on the principal's task force for healthier lifestyles. If he chooses 3 of them at random to shoot a TV commercial for morning announcements, what is the probability that Joseph, Heidi, and Katy are chosen?

   A $\frac{3}{120}$ **B** $\frac{1}{40}$ **C** $\frac{1}{5040}$ **D** $\frac{1}{120}$

   7. _____

8. Point X is chosen at random on $\overline{PY}$. Find $P(X$ is on $\overline{LY}$).

   F 0.79   **H** 0.5

   G 0.74   **J** 0.37

   $\overset{3}{\underset{P \quad\quad L}{\bullet\!\!-\!\!-\!\!-\!\!-\!\!\bullet}} \overset{7}{\underset{J}{-\!\!-\!\!-\!\!-\!\!-\!\!-\!\!\bullet}} \overset{4}{\underset{Y}{-\!\!-\!\!-\!\!-\!\!\bullet}}$

   8. _____

9. Use the spinner shown. Find the probability the pointer lands on purple.

   A $\frac{4}{5}$ **C** $\frac{2}{9}$

   B $\frac{80}{180}$ **D** $\frac{4}{9}$

   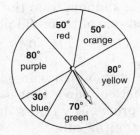

   9. _____

Assessment

13 Chapter 13 Test, Form 2A (continued)

10. Jason made 60% of his shots at the goal last year in ice hockey. To find the probability of whether or not Jason makes his next goal, which simulation should be used?
    F spinning a spinner 100 times with sectors of 144° and 216°
    G spinning a spinner 100 times with sectors of 40° and 60°
    H tossing a coin 60 times
    J choosing from a bag of 60 marbles 40 times

10. _____

11. Find the probability of a point chosen at random being in the shaded area of the diagram at the right.

    A $\frac{4}{9}$ C $\frac{1}{9}$
    B $\frac{1}{4}$ D $\frac{1}{2}$

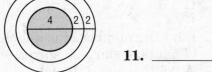

11. _____

12. According to The Law of Large Numbers, what happens to the average value the more trials you conduct?
    F approaches infinity   H approaches experimental value
    G approaches expected value   J decreases

12. _____

13. Calculate the expected value, $E(X)$, of a dart game with the board shown.
    A 287.5   C 222.22
    B 200   D 155.56

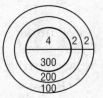

13. _____

14. A card is drawn from a standard deck and not replaced. Then a second card is drawn. What is the probability the first card is an ace and the second card is a king?
    F $\frac{1}{2652}$ G $\frac{4}{867}$ H $\frac{1}{663}$ J $\frac{4}{663}$

14. _____

15. What is the probability of rolling two sixes if you roll a pair of dice?
    A $\frac{1}{6}$ B $\frac{1}{36}$ C $\frac{1}{3}$ D $\frac{1}{18}$

15. _____

16. What is the probability of drawing an ace or a spade from a standard deck of cards?
    F $\frac{1}{52}$ G $\frac{17}{52}$ H $\frac{4}{13}$ J $\frac{3}{169}$

16. _____

17. What is the probability rolling a pair of dice and *not* rolling a 6?
    A $\frac{5}{6}$ B $\frac{1}{6}$ C $\frac{25}{36}$ D $\frac{1}{36}$

17. _____

18. In Daniel's senior class of 100 students, 91% went to the senior picnic. If 2 people are chosen at random from the entire class, what is the probability that at least one of them did not go to the senior picnic?
    F 0.09   G 0.17   H 0.18   J 0.91

18. _____

Bonus The net for a cube with 5 inches on each side is unfolded and glued to a rectangular piece of paper that is 30 inches long and 30 inches wide. What is the probability that a dart thrown at the paper will not land on the net of the cube?

B: _____

13   Chapter 13 Test, Form 2B

Write the letter for the correct answer in the blank at the right of each question.

1. Carlos can choose from a beef or turkey burger and from a wheat or a white roll. How many different burgers can he make?

  A 2   **B** 3   **C** 4   **D** 8   1. _____

2. If a die is rolled 3 times, what is the number of possible outcomes?

  F 6.3   **G** 3^6 **H** 6!   **J** 216   2. _____

3. Find the number of possible outcomes for a weekend camping trip from 4 places to camp, 2 types of sleeping bags, 3 types of tents, and 5 different meal plans.

  A 120   **B** 90   **C** 4!   **D** $4 - 2!$ 3. _____

4. The 5 posters made for spirit week are being hung in the front hall. What is the probability the largest poster will be in the center and the next largest will be on its left?

  F $\frac{1}{60}$ **G** $\frac{1}{120}$ **H** $\frac{1}{20}$ **J** 120   4. _____

5. Six people are randomly sat at a round table. What is the probability the people are sitting in alphabetical order?

  A $\frac{1}{6}$ **B** $\frac{1}{120}$ **C** $\frac{1}{720}$ **D** $\frac{6}{120}$ 5. _____

6. What is the probability that a randomly selected permutation of the letters A, A, C, C, L, L, O, R, T, U would spell "calculator"?

  F $\frac{1}{453,600}$ **G** $\frac{3}{362,880}$ **H** $\frac{1}{362,8800}$ **J** $\frac{1}{604,800}$ 6. _____

7. Three of the 10 people in the Latin club are chosen at random to wear togas to school to promote the club. What is the probability that Joseph, Heidi, and Katy are chosen?

  A $\frac{3}{120}$ **B** $\frac{1}{40}$ **C** $\frac{1}{120}$ **D** $\frac{1}{5040}$ 7. _____

8. Point X is chosen at random on $\overline{YM}$. Find $P(X$ is on $\overline{YZ})$.

  F 0.22   **H** 0.52

  G 0.29   **J** 0.56   8. _____

(diagram: points Y, Z, P, M on a line with segments 2, 5, 2)

9. A spinner contains a sector shaded red with a central angle that is 50°. What is the probability that the spinner will land on red?

  A $\frac{1}{5}$ **B** $\frac{1}{2}$ **C** $\frac{50}{180}$ **D** $\frac{5}{36}$ 9. _____

10. Find the probability that a point chosen at random inside the circle also lies in the square.

  F 5%   **G** 14%

  G 11%   **H** 20%   10. _____

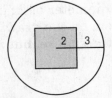

Assessment

13 Chapter 13 Test, Form 2B (continued)

11. Last year 45% of the books ordered for the school library were fiction. Which model would could be used in a simulation conducted to find the probability of whether or not a book chosen randomly from this years order will be fiction?
    A a spinner with sectors of 45° and 55°
    B a spinner with sectors of 162° and 198°
    C tossing a coin 45 times
    D a bag of 45 marbles

11. _____

12. The Law of Large Numbers states that the more trials of a simulation you conduct, the difference between the average and expected values:
    F decreases   H remains the same
    G increases   J approaches infinity

12. _____

13. Calculate the expected value, $E(X)$, of a dart game with the board shown.
    A 112   C 169.4
    B 200   D 228.1

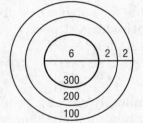

13. _____

14. A card is drawn from a standard deck and not replaced. Then a second card is drawn. What is the probability both cards are hearts?
    F $\frac{13}{204}$ G $\frac{3}{52}$ H $\frac{1}{17}$ J $\frac{1}{16}$

14. _____

15. A pair of dice are rolled. What is the probability that a 1 is showing on both dice?
    A $\frac{1}{36}$ B $\frac{1}{6}$ C $\frac{1}{18}$ D $\frac{1}{3}$

15. _____

16. What is the probability of drawing a 2 or a heart from a standard deck of cards?
    F $\frac{3}{169}$ G $\frac{1}{52}$ H $\frac{17}{52}$ J $\frac{4}{13}$

16. _____

17. What is the probability of drawing a card from a standard deck and *not* drawing a face card?
    A $\frac{3}{4}$ B $\frac{10}{13}$ C $\frac{12}{52}$ D $\frac{3}{13}$

17. _____

18. In Maya's senior class of 100 students, 89% attended the senior brunch. If 2 students are chosen at random from the entire class, what is the probability that at least one of students did not attend the brunch?
    F 0.11   G 0.21   H 0.22   J 0.89

18. _____

Bonus A circle with a diameter of $2x$ is inscribed in a square. A point is chosen at random on the drawing. What is the probability that the point is inside the square, but *not* inside of the circle?

B: _____

13   Chapter 13 Test, Form 2C

1. A spinner has 4 equal sectors numbered 1 to 4. The spinner is spun twice. Make an organized list to represent the sample space.

1. _____

2. A die is rolled 4 times. How many outcomes are possible?

2. _____

3. Carl is creating greeting cards from a website. He has to choose from the following: 2 types of paper, 5 different fonts, 5 different greetings inside, and 3 types of envelopes. How many different cards can Carl create?

3. _____

4. Minnie is stacking her 5 textbooks on the shelf in her locker. What is the probability that her Chemistry book will be on top of the stack and her Geometry book will be on the bottom?

4. _____

5. As part of the National Honors Society ceremony, the six new members are randomly arranged in a circle. What is the probability that the new members are arranged in height order?

5. _____

6. What is the probability that a randomly selected permutation of the letters shown below will spell "permutation"?

    A E I M N O P R T T U

6. _____

7. Three of the ten members of the AV club are randomly chosen to read the morning announcements for the month of May. What is the probability that the three freshmen in the club are chosen?

7. _____

8. Point K is chosen at random on $\overline{XY}$. Find $P(K$ is on $\overline{XP})$.

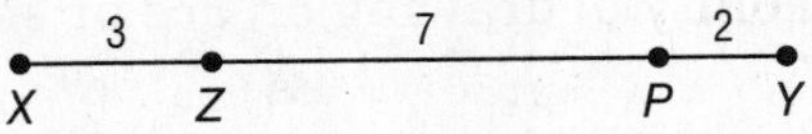

          3   7   2
      X   Z   P   Y

8. _____

9. At Khyree's favorite pizza buffet, the pizza is completely replaced every 20 minutes during the 3 hour lunch rush. If he arrives at a random time during the lunch rush, what is the probability he will have to wait longer than 5 minutes for fresh pizza?

9. _____

10. In a circular spinner, the sector colored yellow as a central angle of 85°. What is the probability the pointer will land on yellow?

10. _____

Assessment

13   Chapter 13 Test, Form 2C *(continued)*

11. Jake designed a simulation using random numbers 0 to 9 to represent the data in the table. Assign the random numbers to each outcome.

Outcome	Theoretical Probability
Red	20%
Blue	30%
Green	10%
Yellow	10%
Orange	30%

11. _____

For Questions 12 and 13, use the frequency table and the following information.

Simon used his statistics from last year and created a simulation using a spinner to find the theoretical probability of his hitting a home run this season.

Outcome	Tally	Frequency
did not reach base	卌 卌 卌	15
single	卌 卌 卌 卌 卌	25
double	卌 卌 ||	12
triple	||	2
home run			1

12. What is the theoretical probability of Simon hitting a home run this season?

12. _____

13. About what size should you expect the central angle that designates the sector that represented 'double' be in the spinner Simon designed for his simulation?

13. _____

14. Two cards are drawn from a standard deck without replacement. What is the probability the first card is an ace and the second card is a king?

14. _____

15. A pair of dice are rolled. What is the probability that a 6 is rolled on each die?

15. _____

16. What is the probability of drawing an ace or spade from a standard deck of cards?

16. _____

For Questions 17 and 18, use the dart game at the right.

17. Calculate the expected value, $E(X)$, of the dart game.

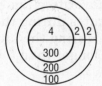

17. _____

18. Find the probability of a point chosen at random being in the 100 point area.

18. _____

19. What is the probability rolling a pair of dice and *not* rolling a 6?

19. _____

20. Of the 100 bags of food the junior class created for the food bank, 91% contained peanut-free items. If two of the bags are chosen at random, what is the probability that at least one of the bags contains peanut-free items?

20. _____

Bonus A circle with a diameter of $4x$ is inscribed in a square. A point is chosen at random on the drawing. What is the probability that the point is inside the square but *not* inside the circle?

B. _____

13   Chapter 13 Test, Form 2D

1. A spinner has 4 equal sized sectors colored red, blue, yellow, and green. The spinner is spun twice. Make an organized list to represent the sample space.

1. _____

2. A die is rolled 3 times. How many outcomes are possible?

2. _____

3. Janie brought 4 pairs of pants, 2 skirts, 3 shirts, and 5 pairs of shoes on summer vacation. How many different outfits can Janie create if she wears parts or a skirt, a shirt, and a pair of shoes?

3. _____

4. Hannah and her four best friends are lining up for a picture. What is the probability that Hannah will stand in the center and Katie will be on her left?

4. _____

5. The hostess sat your group of 6 at a round table. If you all choose your seats randomly, what is the probability you are sitting in alphabetical order?

5. _____

6. What is the probability that a randomly selected permutation of the letters A, A, C, C, L, L, O, R, T, U would spell "calculator"?

6. _____

7. Three of the 10 students in the Latin club are chosen at random to wear togas to school to promote the club. What is the probability that Joseph, Heidi, and Katy are chosen?

7. _____

8. Point X is chosen at random on $\overline{MP}$. Find $P(X$ is on $\overline{MN})$.

M   N   Q P
  2   5   1

8. _____

9. Find the probability of a point chosen at random being in the shaded area.

5 / 60°

9. _____

10. In a 3-minute traffic cycle the light is green for 1 minute, 27 seconds; yellow for 6 seconds; and red for 1 minute, 27 seconds. If you arrive at the light at a random time, what is the probability that the light will be red?

10. _____

11. A circular spinner is created so that there are 6 equal spaces. If two of the spaces are red, two of the spaces are blue, and two of the spaces are orange, find the probability the pointer lands on orange.

11. _____

13   Chapter 13 Test, Form 2D *(continued)*

12. Urmi made 45% of her free throw shots last year. Describe a spinner that could be used in a simulation to determine the theoretical probability of Urmi making a free throw.

12. _____

For Questions 13 and 14, use the frequency table and the following information.

Annalee used her statistics from last year and created a simulation using a spinner to find the theoretical probability of her making a goal this season.

Outcome	Tally	Frequency
makes goal free	|||| |||| |||| |||| |||| ||	26
misses goal	|||| |||| ||||	14
Total		40

13. What is the theoretical probability of Annalee making a goal this season?

13. _____

14. About what size should you expect the central angle that designates the sector that represents 'makes goal' be in the spinner Annalee designed for the simulation?

14. _____

15. A card is drawn from a standard deck and not replaced. Then a second card is drawn. What is the probability that both cards are hearts?

15. _____

16. What is the probability when a pair of dice is rolled, both show a 1?

16. _____

17. What is the probability of drawing a 2 or a heart from a standard deck of cards?

17. _____

18. What is the probability of drawing a card from a standard deck and *not* drawing a face card?

18. _____

19. Calculate the expected value, $E(X)$, of the dart game.

19. _____

20. In Maya's sophomore class of 100 students, 89% wore their school T-shirt on school spirit day. If 2 people are chosen at random from the entire class, what is the probability that at least one of them did not wear their school T-shirt?

20. _____

Bonus A coordinate grid is drawn with a maximum of 10 and a minimum of −10 on the axes. The coordinates $A(0, 2)$, $B(2, 0)$, $C(0, -2)$, and $D(-2, 0)$ are graphed to form a square. If a point is randomly chosen on the coordinate grid, what is the probability the point is inside of square $ABCD$?

B: _____

SCORE _____

13 Chapter 13 Test, Form 3

1. Write an organized list to show the sample space for choosing an outfit from black or tan pants and a black or tan shirt.

1. _____

2. What is the number of possible outcomes for spinning a spinner with six equal sections and then rolling a die?

2. _____

3. How many single-scoop cones could be made from a choice of 2 types of cones, 3 flavors of ice cream, and optional toppings of peanuts and/or sprinkles?

3. _____

4. The 5 senior members of the softball team line up to take a picture. What is the probability the center fielder is in the center and the first baseman is to next to her?

4. _____

5. The hostess sat your group of 6 family members at a round table. If you all choose your seats randomly, what is the probability you sit on your mom's right?

5. _____

6. Using the letters and numbers A, D, L, 8, 4, and 8, what is the probability that a 6-space license plate would spell L84AD8?

6. _____

7. Points A, B, C, D, E, and F are coplanar, but no 3 are collinear. What is the probability that a line segment chosen at random would be $\overline{AB}$?

7. _____

8. Point X is chosen at random on $\overline{AB}$. Use <, >, or = to compare.

```
    3       5      2    2
A●──────C●──────────D●───E●───●B
```

$P(X$ is on $\overline{AD})$ $P(X$ is on $\overline{CB})$

8. _____

9. Carla is has programmed her screen saver to change colors. In a 2-minute cycle, the screen is green for 40 seconds, purple for 6 seconds, pink for 14 seconds, then green for 14 seconds, purple for 6 seconds, and pink for 40 seconds. If she sits down at her computer at a random time, what is the probability her screen will be green?

9. _____

10. Using the spinner shown, what is the probability the pointer lands on yellow or red?

10. _____

Assessment

11. Find the probability of a point chosen at random being in the shaded region.

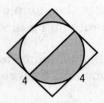

4   4

11. _____

12. What method can be used to simulate an experiment with two equally likely outcomes?

12. _____

13. If a simulation was conducted with 50 trials and a certain outcome occurred 12 times, does that show a *theoretical probability*, an *experimental probability* or an *expected value of 0.24*?

13. _____

14. Is the following statement *true* or *false*?

The Law of Large Numbers states that since an expected value is an average, it does not have to be equal to a possible value of the random variable.

14. _____

15. Calculate the expected value for each throw of this dart game.

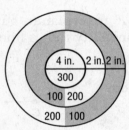

4 in. 2 in. 2 in.
300
100 200
200 100

15. _____

16. What is the probability that if 2 cards are drawn from a standard deck without replacement, the first card is a heart and the second card is a spade?

16. _____

17. In a game a pair of dice are rolled. Find the probability the sum of the numbers rolled is 8.

17. _____

18. If only one die is rolled, what is the probability of rolling a 2 or a prime number?

18. _____

19. When drawing from a standard deck of 52 cards, what is the probability of not drawing a face card?

19. _____

20. A survey shows that 72% of students approve of the choices available in the school cafeteria. If two people are randomly chosen out of a group of 100, find the probability that exactly one person approves of the choices available.

20. _____

Bonus Determine whether the following is *sometimes*, *always*, or *never* mutually exclusive: choosing a rhombus that is a parallelogram and a rhombus that is a square.

B: _____

13 **Chapter 13 Extended-Response Test**

SCORE _____

Demonstrate your knowledge by giving a clear, concise solution to each problem. Be sure to include all relevant drawings and justify your answers. You may show your solution in more than one way or investigate beyond the requirements of the problem.

1. For a math project each student is required to choose an obtuse triangle, a right triangle, or an acute triangle, and then choose a parallelogram, a rectangle, a rhombus, or a square.

   a. Draw a tree diagram to represent the possible outcomes.

   b. What is the probability a student will choose an acute triangle or a square?

2. Describe an outcome for each situation.

   a. two cards randomly chosen from a standard deck so that the cards being chosen are independent events

   b. two cards randomly chosen from a standard deck so that the cards being chosen are dependant events

3.

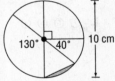

   a. Explain how to find the probability that a point chosen at random lies in the shaded region.

   b. Find the probability that a point chosen at random lies in the shaded region.

13 Standardized Test Practice
(Chapters 1–13)

Part 1: Multiple Choice
Instructions: Fill in the appropriate circle for the best answer.

1. If $\overline{DG}$ bisects $\angle EDF$, which is a true statement? (Lesson 5-1)

   A B is the incenter of $\triangle DEF$.

   B $DB = BG$

   C $\overline{BE} \cong \overline{BF}$

   D B is equidistant from $\overline{DE}$ and $\overline{DF}$.

   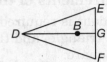

   1. Ⓐ Ⓑ Ⓒ Ⓓ

2. If $\overline{ST}$ is a midsegment of $\triangle PQR$, which is a true statement? (Lesson 7-4)

   F $PQ = 2ST$ **H** $3PQ = 4ST$

   G $2PQ = ST$ **J** $4PQ = 3ST$

   2. Ⓕ Ⓖ Ⓗ Ⓙ

3. Classify $\triangle HJK$ by its sides if its vertices are $H(6, -2)$, $J(-9, -10)$, and $K(-9, 6)$. (Lesson 4-1)

   A equilateral

   B scalene

   C isosceles

   D right

   3. Ⓐ Ⓑ Ⓒ Ⓓ

4. Find the circumference of $\odot G$. (Lesson 10-1)

   F 9π in.

   G 12π in.

   H 15π in.

   J 30π in.

   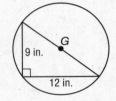

   4. Ⓕ Ⓖ Ⓗ Ⓙ

5. If a line is tangent to a circle, then it is ___?___ to the radius drawn to the point of tangency. (Lesson 10-5)

   A perpendicular

   B parallel

   C congruent

   D not related

   5. Ⓐ Ⓑ Ⓒ Ⓓ

6. Find the area of a circle with a diameter of 28 meters. (Lesson 11-4)

   F 49π m^2

   G 196π m^2

   H 784π m^2

   J 3136π m^2

   6. Ⓕ Ⓖ Ⓗ Ⓙ

7. Which figures are needed to make a net for the solid? (Lesson 12-1)

   A 2 trapezoids and 4 rectangles

   B 6 rectangles

   C 4 trapezoids and 2 rectangles

   D 6 trapezoids

   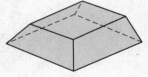

   7. Ⓐ Ⓑ Ⓒ Ⓓ

8. Find the volume of a right circular cone with a height of 14 inches and a diameter of 10 inches. Round to the nearest tenth. (Lesson 12-5)

   F 183.3 in^3 **G** 366.5 in^3 **H** 733.0 in^3 **J** 1466.1 in^3

   8. Ⓕ Ⓖ Ⓗ Ⓙ

13 Standardized Test Practice (continued)

9. If $\angle C$ and $\angle D$ are congruent supplementary angles and $m\angle C = 3x + 72$, find x. (Lesson 2-8)

  A 6   **B** 36   **C** 54   **D** 85   **9.** Ⓐ Ⓑ Ⓒ Ⓓ

10. Determine the slope of the line that contains $J(24, -5)$ and $K(16, -18)$. (Lesson 3-3)

  F $-\dfrac{23}{8}$ **G** $-\dfrac{8}{17}$ **H** $\dfrac{8}{13}$ **J** $\dfrac{13}{8}$ **10.** Ⓕ Ⓖ Ⓗ Ⓙ

11. In $\odot A$, $m\overarc{BC} = 2x + 16$ and $m\angle BAC = 5x - 98$. Find x. (Lesson 10-2)

  A 22   **B** 27   **C** 38   **D** 46   **11.** Ⓐ Ⓑ Ⓒ Ⓓ

12. Find the area of a rhombus with diagonals that are 24 centimeters and 78 centimeters long. (Lesson 11-2)

  F 234 cm²   **G** 468 cm²   **H** 936 cm²   **J** 1872 cm²   **12.** Ⓕ Ⓖ Ⓗ Ⓙ

13. Find the volume to the nearest tenth. (Lesson 12-4)

  A 452.4 m³   **B** 665.1 m³   **C** 1357.2 m³   **D** 5428.7 m³    **13.** Ⓐ Ⓑ Ⓒ Ⓓ

14. Find the volume to the nearest tenth. (Lesson 12-5)

  F 168 in³   **H** 344 in³

  G 252 in³   **J** 504 in³   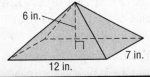 **14.** Ⓕ Ⓖ Ⓗ Ⓙ

Part 2: Gridded Response

Instructions: Enter your answer by writing each digit of the answer in a column box and then shading in the appropriate circle that corresponds to that entry.

15. Find the y-coordinate of the image of $A(3, -5)$ under a rotation of 180° about the origin. (Lesson 9-3)

15.

16. Find x so that the figures are similar. (Lesson 12-8)

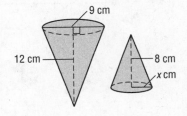

16.

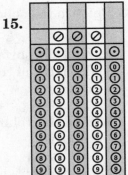

Assessment

13 Standardized Test Practice (continued)

Part 3: Short Response
Instructions: Write your answer in the space provided.

17. A spinner with 6 equal sections, is spun and a coin is tossed. How many outcomes are possible? (Lesson 13-1)

17._____

18. Quadrilateral *PQRS* is inscribed in $\odot O$ so that $\angle S$ and $\angle Q$ are opposite angles, $m\angle Q = 10x - 11$, and $m\angle S = 6x + 27$. Find x. (Lesson 10-4)

18._____

19. Find the area of quadrilateral *CDEF* if the distance from *C* to $\overline{DF}$ is 14 meters. (Lesson 11-2)

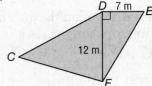

19._____

20. A right cylinder has a height of 7 inches and a base with a diameter of 8 inches. Find the lateral area of the cylinder. Round to the nearest tenth. (Lesson 12-2)

20._____

21. Find the volume of a hemisphere with a diameter of 18 feet. Round to the nearest tenth. (Lesson 12-6)

21._____

22. Determine the coordinates of the midpoint of the segment joining $W(2, 4)$ and $X(-1, 7)$. (Lesson 1-3)

22._____

23. Refer to the solid below. Round to the nearest tenth.

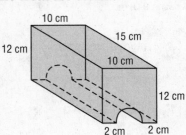

a. Find the surface area of the five flat faces of the solid.
(Lesson 12-2)

23a._____

b. Find the volume of the solid.
(Lesson 12-4)

b._____

c. If this figure was enlarged by a scale factor of 1.5, what would be its new volume? (Lesson 12-8)

c._____

13 **Unit 4 Test**
(Chapters 10–13)

For Questions 1 and 2, refer to the figure.

1. In $\odot J$, $HK = 28$ centimeters and $m\widehat{NK} = 72$. Find $m\angle NJK$ and the length of $\widehat{NK}$.

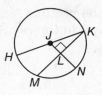

1. _____

2. If radius $\overline{HJ}$ measures 20 units, $JL = 12$, and $m\angle HJN = 126.9$, find LK, MK, and $m\widehat{MNK}$.

2. _____

3. A regular hexagon is inscribed in $\odot P$. Find the area of the shaded region.

3. _____

4. Find the area of the irregular figure.

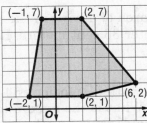

4. _____

5. Find the probability that a point chosen at random lies in the shaded region.

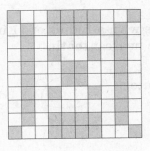

5. _____

For Questions 6 and 7, refer to the figure.

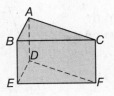

6. Identify the solid and name its bases.

6. _____

7. Find the surface area of the solid to the nearest tenth if $AB = 8$, $AC = 25$, $CF = 14$, and $EF = 25$.

7. _____

8. A card is chosen from a standard deck. What is the probability the card is an ace or a heart?

8. _____

9. Find the lateral area of a rectangular prism with base 4.8 inches by 6.2 inches and height 5.9 inches.

9. _____

10. The lateral area of a right cylinder is 180.2π square meters and its height is 10.6 meters. Find the radius of the base of the cylinder.

10. _____

Assessment

13 Unit 4 Test (continued)

11. Find the surface area of the regular pentagonal pyramid. Round to the nearest tenth.

10 ft
4 ft

11._____

12. Mark is cutting colored paper to make conical party hats for his daughter's birthday party. He wants to make them with a diameter of 9 inches and a height of 12 inches. What is the lateral area of one party hat?

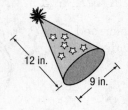
12 in.
9 in.

12._____

13. Find the outer surface area of a bowl in the shape of a perfect hemisphere with diameter 36 centimeters. Round to the nearest tenth.

13._____

14. Sandra is packing a box with dimensions 54 inches by 78 inches by 42 inches. What is the maximum volume in cubic **feet** that this box can hold? Round to the nearest tenth.

14._____

15. Find the volume of a cone with a radius of 11 inches and a height of 15 inches to the nearest tenth.

15._____

16. Which figure has the greater volume, the sphere or the cylinder?

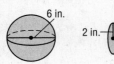
6 in.
2 in.
10 in.

16._____

17. Determine whether the pair of cones is *similar*, *congruent*, or *neither*.

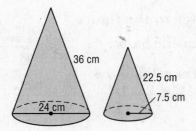
36 cm
24 cm
22.5 cm
7.5 cm

17._____

18. Chris found that last year he made 40% of his freethrows. Design a simulation to find the experimental probability of him making a free throw.

18._____

NAME _____ DATE _____ PERIOD _____

13-1 Study Guide and Intervention

Representing Sample Spaces

Represent a Sample Space The sample space of an experiment is the set of all possible outcomes. A sample space can be found using an organized list, table, or tree diagram.

Example Maurice packs suits, shirts, and ties that can be mixed and matched. Using the packing list at the right, draw a tree diagram to represent the sample space for business suit combinations.

Maurice's Packing List
1. Suits: Gray, black, khaki
2. Shirts: White, light blue
3. Ties: Striped (But optional)

The sample space is the result of three stages:
- Suit color (G, B, or K)
- Shirt color (W or L)
- Tie (T or NT)

Draw a tree diagram with three stages.

Exercises

Represent the sample space for each experiment by making an organized list, a table, and a tree diagram.

1. The baseball team can wear blue or white shirts with blue or white pants.

BB, BW, WB, WW

2. The dance club is going to see either *Sleeping Beauty* or *The Nutcracker* at either Symphony Hall or The Center for the Arts.

SS, SC, NS, NC

3. Mikey's baby sister can drink either apple juice or milk from a bottle or a toddler cup.

AB, AT, MB, MT

4. The first part of the test consisted of two true-or-false questions.

TT, TF, FT, FF

Chapter 13   5   *Glencoe Geometry*

NAME _____ DATE _____ PERIOD _____

13 Anticipation Guide
Probability and Measurement

Step 1 *Before you begin Chapter 1*

- Read each statement.
- Decide whether you Agree (A) or Disagree (D) with the statement.
- Write A or D in the first column OR if you are not sure whether you agree or disagree, write NS (Not Sure).

STEP 1 A, D, or NS	Statement	STEP 2 A or D
	1. A sample space can be represented using a tree diagram.	A
	2. The Fundamental Counting Principle will find the number of possible outcomes of an event.	A
	3. The number 0 factorial, or 0!, is equal to 0.	D
	4. In a permutation, the order of the objects is not important.	D
	5. When designing a simulation, always state any assumptions necessary.	A
	6. The expected value of a random variable is the median value of a variable that one expects after repeating an experiment.	D
	7. Two events are considered independent if the probability that one occurs does not affect the probability the other occurs.	A
	8. Two events are considered mutually exclusive if they can happen at the same time and have similar outcomes.	D

Step 2 *After you complete Chapter 13*

- Reread each statement and complete the last column by entering an A or a D.
- Did any of your opinions about the statements change from the first column?
- For those statements that you mark with a D, use a piece of paper to write an example of why you disagree.

Chapter 13   3   *Glencoe Geometry*

Answers

13-1 Skills Practice

NAME _____ DATE _____ PERIOD _____

Representing Sample Spaces

Represent the sample space for each experiment by making an organized list, a table, and a tree diagram.

1. Michelle could take a summer job in California or Arizona at a hotel or a bed-and-breakfast.

CH, CB, AH, AB

Outcomes	Hotel	B & B
California	C, H	C, B
Arizona	A, H	A, B

State: C → H, B; A → H, B
Type

2. Jeremy could go to baseball or soccer camp as a counselor or an assistant director.

BC, BA, SC, SA

Outcomes	Couns.	Asst.
Baseball	B, C	B, A
Soccer	S, C	S, A

Sport: B → C, A; S → C, A
Position

3. Brad could buy his mom a $25 or $50 gift card for a spa or a housecleaning service.

$25 S, $25 H, $50 S, $50 H

Outcomes	Spa	House cleaning
$25	$25, S	$25, H
$50	$50, S	$50, H

Dollar amt.: $25 → S, H; $50 → S, H
Gift

Find the number of possible outcomes for each situation.

4. Marie's family is buying a house. They must choose one from each category.

House Plans	Number of Choices
Subdivision location	4
Floor plans	5
Garage size	2
Front yard landscape package	3
Backyard pool package	3

360

5. Mr. Thomson is choosing his cable TV. He must choose one from each category.

Cable TV Plans	Number of Choices
Channel packages	16
DVR system	3
Contract length	3
Service contract	2
Include phone	2
Include Internet	2

1152

6. Valentine gift sets come with a choice of 4 different teddy bears, 8 types of candy, 5 balloon designs, and 3 colors of roses.

480

7. Joni wears a school uniform that consists of a skirt or pants, a white shirt, a blue jacket or sweater, white socks and black shoes. She has 3 pairs of pants, 3 skirts, 6 shirts, 2 jackets, 2 sweaters, 6 pairs of socks and 3 pairs of black shoes.

2592

Chapter 13   7   *Glencoe Geometry*

13-1 Study Guide and Intervention *(continued)*

NAME _____ DATE _____ PERIOD _____

Representing Sample Spaces

Fundamental Counting Principle The number of all possible outcomes for an experiment can be found by multiplying the number of possible outcomes from each stage or event.

Example The pattern for a certain license plate is 3 letters followed by 3 numbers. The letter "O" is not used as any of the letters and the number "0" is not used as any of the numbers. Any other letter or number can be used multiple times. How many license plates can be created with this pattern?

Use the Fundamental Counting Principle.

1st Space	2nd Space	3rd Space	4th Space	5th Space	6th Space	Possible Outcomes
25	× 25	× 25	× 9	× 9	× 9	= 11,390,625

So 11,390,625 license plates can be created with this pattern.

Exercises

Find the number of possible outcomes for each situation.

1. A room is decorated with one choice from each category.

Bedroom Décor	Number of Choices
Paint color	8
Comforter set	6
Sheet set	8
Throw rug	5
Lamp	3
Wall hanging	5

28,800

2. A lunch at Lincoln High School contains one choice from each category.

Cafeteria Meal	Number of Choices
Main dish	3
Side dish	4
Vegetable	2
Salad	2
Salad Dressing	3
Dessert	2
Drink	3

864

3. In a catalog of outdoor patio plans, there are 4 types of stone, 3 types of edgers, 5 dining sets and 6 grills. Carl plans to order one item from each category.

360

4. The drama club held tryouts for 6 roles in a one-act play. Five people auditioned for lead female, 3 for lead male, 8 for the best friend, 4 for the mom, 2 for the dad, and 3 for the crazy aunt.

2880

Chapter 13   6   *Glencoe Geometry*

NAME _____ DATE _____ PERIOD _____

13-1 Practice

Representing Sample Spaces

Represent the sample space for each experiment by making an organized list, a table, and a tree diagram.

1. Tavya can spend the summer with her cousins or her grandparents at the lake or at the beach.

CL, CB, GL, GB

Outcomes	Lake	Beach
Cousins	C,L	C,B
Grandparents	G,L	G,B

2. Jordan can write his final essay in class or at home on a scientific or an historical topic.

SC, SH, HC, HH

Outcomes	In Class	At Home
Scientific	S,C	S,H
Historical	H,C	H,H

3. Julio can join the Air Force or the Army before or after college.

**AF, BC; AF, AC;
A, BC; A, AC**

Outcomes	Before College	After College
Air Force	AF, BC	AF, AC
Army	A, BC	A, AC

Find the number of possible outcomes for each situation.

4. Josh is making a stuffed animal.

Animal Options	Number of Choices
Animals	10
Type of stuffing	3
Sound effect	5
Eye color	3
Outfit	20

9000

5. Kelley is buying an ice cream cone. Assume one of each category is ordered.

Ice Cream	Number of Choices
Type of cone	3
Flavors	20
Cookie toppings	4
Candy toppings	8

1920

6. Movie-themed gift baskets come with a choice of one of each of the following: 4 flavors of popcorn, 4 different DVDs, 4 types of drinks, and 8 different kinds of candy.

512

7. **INTERNSHIP** Jack is choosing an internship program that could take place in 3 different months, in 4 different departments of 3 different firms. Jack is only available to complete his internship in July. How many different outcomes are there for Jack's internship?

12

Chapter 13   8   *Glencoe Geometry*

NAME _____ DATE _____ PERIOD _____

13-1 Word Problem Practice

Representing Sample Spaces

1. **SCHOOL SUPPLIES** Eva is shopping for school supplies. She has a choice of one of each of the following: 6 backpacks, 8 notebooks, 3 pencil cases, 3 brands of pencils, 8 brands of pens, 4 types of calculator, and 4 colors of highlighter. How many different choices does she have for school supplies?

55,296

2. **LAPTOPS** Chloe is buying a laptop. She has a choice of 3 hard drive sizes, 3 processor speeds, 4 colors, 2 screen sizes, 2 warranty options, and 4 cases. She knows she wants a blue laptop with the longest warranty. How many choices does she have for laptops?

72

3. **BOARD GAMES** Below is a spinner used in a board game. If the spinner is spun 4 times, how many different possible outcomes are there?

1296

4. **BASKETBALL** In the NBA there must be a minimum of 14 players on a team's roster. A team has the minimum number of players where 3 are centers, 4 are power forwards, 2 are small forwards, 3 are shooting guards, and the rest are point guards. For this situation, how many different possible outcomes are there?

Source: *NBA Players Association*

144

5. **VACATION RENTAL** A brochure describes available vacation rentals in Colorado and Florida. In Colorado you can choose a 1 or 2 week stay in a 1- or 2-bedroom suite. In Florida you can choose a 1, 2 or 3 week stay in a 2- or 3-bedroom suite, along the beach or not.

a. How many outcomes are available in Colorado?

4

b. How many outcomes are available in Florida?

12

c. How many total outcomes are available?

16

Chapter 13   9   *Glencoe Geometry*

Lesson 13-2

NAME _____ DATE _____ PERIOD _____

13-2 Study Guide and Intervention

Probability with Permutations and Combinations

Probability Using Permutations A permutation is an arrangement of objects where order is important. To find the number of permutations of a group of objects, use the **factorial**. A factorial is written using a number and !. The following are permutation formulas:

$n! = n \cdot (n-1) \cdot (n-2) \cdot \ldots \cdot 2 \cdot 1$

$5! = 5 \cdot 4 \cdot 3 \cdot 2 \cdot 1 = 120$

n distinct objects taken r at a time	$_nP_r = \dfrac{n!}{(n-r)!}$
n objects, where one object is repeated r_1 times, another is repeated r_2 times, and so on	$\dfrac{n!}{r_1! \cdot r_2! \cdot \ldots \cdot r_k!}$
n objects arranged in a circle with no fixed reference point	$\dfrac{n!}{n}$ or $(n-1)!$

Example The cheer squad is made up of 12 girls. A captain and a co-captain are selected at random. What is the probability that Chantel and Cadence are chosen as leaders?

Find the number of possible outcomes.   Find the number of favorable outcomes.

$_{12}P_2 = \dfrac{12!}{(12-2)!} = \dfrac{12!}{10!} = 12 \cdot 11 = 132$ $2! = 2$

The probability of Chantel and Cadence being chosen is

$\dfrac{\text{favorable outcomes}}{\text{total number of outcomes}} = \dfrac{2}{132} = \dfrac{1}{66}$

Exercises

1. **BOOKS** You have a textbook for each of the following subjects: Spanish, English, Chemistry, Geometry, History, and Psychology. If you choose 4 of these at random to arrange on a shelf, what is the probability that the Geometry textbook will be first from the left and the Chemistry textbook will be second from the left?

$\dfrac{1}{30}$

2. **CLUBS** The Service Club is choosing members at random to attend one of four conferences in LA, Atlanta, Chicago, and New York. There are 20 members in the club. What is the probability that Lana, Sherry, Miguel, and Jerome are chosen for these trips?

$\dfrac{1}{4845}$

3. **TELEPHONE NUMBERS** What is the probability that a 7-digit telephone number generated using the digits 2, 3, 2, 5, 2, 7, and 3 is the number 222-3357?

$\dfrac{1}{420}$

4. **DINING OUT** A group of 4 girls and 4 boys is randomly seated at a round table. What is the probability that the arrangement is boy-girl-boy-girl?

$\dfrac{4}{35}$

Chapter 13   11   *Glencoe Geometry*

NAME _____ DATE _____ PERIOD _____

13-1 Enrichment

Traveling Salesman Problem

A traveling salesperson plans to sell a product in several different cities. The salesperson wants to find the shortest route to visit each city, and then return to the starting point. How does the salesperson find the shortest distance to travel to each city?

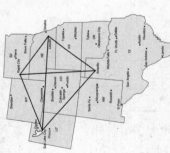

This problem, called the Traveling Salesman Problem, might seem simple, but in fact finding efficient solutions have proven to be very difficult. To date, computers running through the entire **solution space** or **sample space**, of the problem, have arrived at a solution. The computer looks at all possible combinations of cities to visit, computes each combination's length, then finds the shortest distance. Even with the help of computers, however, is not clear if the most efficient general solution has been found.

Example Find the number of ways a person can visit 5 different cities and then return to the first city.

If a person starts at one city there are 4 other cities to visit. Then there are 3 cities and after that 2 cities and then one city. After that they must return to the original city. So:

First	Second	Third	Fourth	
4	• 3	• 2	• 1	= 24

There are 24 different ways to visit 5 cities.

Exercises

Find the sample space of visiting each of the *n* cities and returning to the first city.

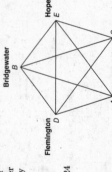

1. $n = 7$ 2. $n = 3$ 3. $n = 8$

720   2   5040

4. $n = 11$ 5. $n = 12$ 6. $n = 4$

3,628,800   399,168,800   6

Chapter 13   10   *Glencoe Geometry*

NAME _____ DATE _____ PERIOD _____

13-2 Study Guide and Intervention (continued)

Probability with Permutations and Combinations

Probability Using Combinations A combination is an arrangement of objects where order is NOT important. To find the number of combinations of n distinct objects taken r at a time, denoted by $_nC_r$, use the formula:

$$_nC_r = \frac{n!}{(n-r)!\,r!}$$

Example Taryn has 15 soccer trophies but she only has room to display 9 of them. If she chooses them at random, what is the probability that each of the trophies from the school invitational from the 1st through 9th grades will be chosen?

Step 1 Since the order does not matter, the number of possible outcomes is

$$_{15}C_9 = \frac{15!}{(15-9)!\,(9!)} = 5005$$

Step 2 There is only one favorable outcome—the 9 specific trophies being chosen.

Step 3 The probability that these 9 trophies are chosen is

$$\frac{\text{number of favorable outcomes}}{\text{total number of outcomes}} = \frac{1}{5005}.$$

Exercises

1. **ICE CREAM** Kali has a choice of 20 flavors for her triple scoop cone. If she chooses flavors at random, what is the probability that the 3 flavors she chooses will be vanilla, chocolate, and strawberry? $\frac{1}{1140}$

2. **PETS** Dani has a dog walking business serving 9 dogs. If she chooses 4 of the dogs at random to take an extra trip to the dog park, what is the probability that Fifi, Gordy, Spike and Fluffy are chosen? $\frac{1}{126}$

3. **CRITIQUE** A restaurant critic has 10 new restaurants to try. If he tries half of them this week, what is the probability that he will choose The Fish Shack, Carly's Place, Chez Henri, Casa de Jorge, and Grillarious? $\frac{1}{252}$

4. **CHARITY** Emily is giving away part of her international doll collection to charity. She has 20 dolls, each from a different country. If she selects 10 of them at random, what is the probability she chooses the ones from Ecuador, Paraguay, Chile, France, Spain, Sweden, Switzerland, Germany, Greece, and Italy? $\frac{1}{184,756}$

5. **ROLLER COASTERS** An amusement park has 12 roller coasters. Four are on the west side of the park, 4 are on the east side, and 4 are centrally located. The park's Maintenance Department randomly chooses 4 roller coasters for upgrades each month. What is the probability that all 4 roller coasters on the west side are chosen in March? $\frac{1}{495}$

NAME _____ DATE _____ PERIOD _____

13-2 Skills Practice

Probabilities With Permutations and Combinations

1. **DISPLAY** The Art Club is displaying the students' works in the main hallway. In a row of 12 randomly ordered paintings, what is the probability that Tim's and Abby's paintings are in the 6th and 7th positions? $\frac{1}{132}$

2. **LINE UP** When the 18 French class students randomly line up for a fire drill, what is the probability that Amy is first and Zach is last in line? $\frac{1}{306}$

3. **TRY-OUTS** Ten students made call-backs for the three lead roles in the school play. What is the probability Sarah, Maria, and Jimenez will be chosen for the leads? $\frac{1}{120}$

4. **SECURITY** Parking stickers contain randomly generated numbers with 5-digits ranging from 1 to 9. No digits are repeated. What is the probability that a randomly generated number is 54321? $\frac{1}{15,120}$

5. **MEETING** Micah is arranging 15 chairs in a circle for an ice breaker game for the first club meeting. If people choose their seats randomly, what is the probability Micah sits in the seat closest to the door? $\frac{1}{15}$

6. **MERRY-GO-ROUND** The mall has a merry-go-round with 12 horses on the outside ring. If 12 people randomly choose those horses, what is the probability they are seated in alphabetical order? $\frac{1}{39,916,800}$

7. **PROMOTION** Tony is promoting his band's first concert. He contacts 10 local radio stations. If 4 of them agree to interview him on the air, what is the probability they are the top 4 stations in the area? $\frac{1}{210}$

8. **TALENT SHOW** The Sign Language Club is choosing 10 of its 15 members to perform at the school talent show. What is the probability that the 10 people chosen are the 10 seniors in the club? $\frac{1}{3003}$

Answers

13-2 Practice

Probability with Permutations and Combinations

NAME _____ DATE _____ PERIOD _____

1. **FORMAL DINING** You are handed 5 pieces of silverware for the formal setting shown. If you guess their placement at random, what is the probability that the knife and spoon are placed correctly? $\frac{1}{20}$

2. **GOLF** The standings list after the first day of a 3-day tournament is shown below. What is the probability that Wyatt, Gabe, and Isaac will all finish in the top 3? $\frac{1}{56}$

DAY 1 STANDINGS	
MCAFEE, DAVID	−3
FORD, GABE	−2
STANDISH, TRISTAN	−2
NICHOLS, WYATT	−1
PURCELL, JACK	−1
ANDERSON, BILL	−1
WRIGHT, ISAAC	−1
FILBERT, MITCH	+1

3. **PHONE NUMBER** What is the probability that a phone number generated using the digits 1, 2, 2, 4, 5, 5, 6, and 2 is the number 654-5222? $\frac{1}{3360}$

4. **LETTERS** Jaclyn bought some decorative letters for a scrapbook project. If she selected a permutation of the letters shown, what is the probability that they would form the word "photography"? $\frac{1}{4,989,600}$

5. **COFFEE BREAK** A group of 6 friends of varying ages meets at a coffee shop and sits in a circle. What is the probability that the youngest member of the group sits in the seat closest to the door? $\frac{1}{6}$

6. **JEWELRY** Bonita bought her mom a charm bracelet. Each charm is labeled with a one-word message. What is the probability that the 5 charms were hung in the order: dream, believe, love, laugh, inspire? $\frac{1}{24}$

7. **COLLEGES** Mark wants to visit the 10 colleges he is considering attending. He can only spend the night at 3 of them. What is the probability that he spends a night at Rutgers University, a night at the University of Miami, and a night at Clemson University? $\frac{1}{120}$

8. **ODD JOBS** Matthew put fliers advertising his lawn service on the doors of 20 families' houses in his neighborhood. If 6 families called him, what is the probability that they were the Thompsons, the Rodriguezes, the Jacksons, the Williamses, the Kryeeks, and the Carpenters? $\frac{1}{38,760}$

Chapter 13   14   Glencoe Geometry

13-2 Word Problem Practice

Probability with Permutations and Combinations

NAME _____ DATE _____ PERIOD _____

1. **RANDOM NUMBERS** A random number generator is a computer program that produces random numbers. What is the probability that it will produce a number less than 1,000 for a 5-digit number? (Hint: 00125 = 125) $\frac{1}{100}$

2. **SCHEDULE** At Randolph High School, there are 17 different classes offered to sophomores each semester. Four classes can be taken each semester and students may not repeat a class during the year. What is the probability of the student taking English, History I, Algebra and Spanish II the first semester and taking History II, Spanish III, Geometry and Biology the next semester? $\frac{1}{1,701,700}$

3. **UNITED NATIONS** The UN Security Council has 5 permanent members and 10 non-permanent members. Italy is one of 192 UN member states and is not a permanent member of the Security Council. What is the probability that Italy is on the Security Council? $\frac{10}{187}$

4. **CARDS** What is the probability in a line of these 5 cards that the ace would be first from the left and the king would be second from the left? $\frac{1}{20}$

5. **GEOMETRY** Points A, B, C, D, and E are coplanar but no 3 are collinear.

   a. What is the total number of lines that can be determined by these points? 10

   b. What is the probability that $\overleftrightarrow{AB}$ would be chosen at random from all of the possible lines formed? $\frac{1}{10}$

Chapter 13   15   Glencoe Geometry

13-2 Enrichment

NAME _____ DATE _____ PERIOD _____

Finding Combinations Using Pascal's Triangle

Blaise Pascal (June 19, 1623 – August 19, 1662) was a French mathematician, philosopher, and physicist. One of his contributions to mathematics is the geometric arrangement of binomial coefficients called Pascal's Triangle. The triangle is constructed in rows by adding terms from previous rows. The first row contains a single digit 1 and is referred to as "Row 0." The outside of the triangle is formed of 1's in a diagonal.

Look at the blank row shown in the diagram. Add the entries from the previous row to find the entries for this row. The next row would then be: 1, 5 (*because 1 + 4 = 5*), 10 (*because 4 + 6 = 10*), 10 (*because 6 + 4 = 10*), 5 (*because 4 + 1 = 5*), and 1. Write these values in the spaces provided.

One use of the values in Pascal's Triangle is finding the number of items taken in combination. For example, the value of $_5C_2$ is found in row 5, entry 2. Remembering that each row begins with entry 0 (which is always equal to 1), The entry found in row 5, entry 2 is 10, $_5C_2 = 10$.

Exercises

Use Pascal's Triangle above to answer the following.

1. Complete the next three rows of Pascal's Triangle.

1		5		10		10		5		1	
1	6		15		20		15		6		1
1	7	21		35		35		21		7	1
1	8	28	56		70		56		28	8	1

2. Use Pascal's Triangle to find $_7C_3$. **35**

3. What do you notice about the values of $_7C_1$ and $_7C_6$? **They're equal.**

4. How many 3-topping pizzas can be made from a choice of 8 toppings? **56**

5. What is the probability that the pizza made in Exercise 4 is a pepperoni, sausage, and onion pizza? $\frac{1}{56}$

6. What is the probability that out of Char's 6 closest friends, Ava and Jenna plan a surprise party for her? $\frac{1}{15}$

Chapter 13   16   *Glencoe Geometry*

13-3 Study Guide and Intervention

NAME _____ DATE _____ PERIOD _____

Geometric Probability

Probability with Length Probability that involves a geometric measure is called geometric probability. One type of measure is length.

Look at line segment $\overline{KL}$.
If a point, M, is chosen at random on the line segment, then
$P(M$ on $\overline{KL}) = \frac{KL}{RS}$.

Example **Point X is chosen at random on $\overline{AD}$. Find the probability that X is on $\overline{AB}$.**

$P(X$ on $\overline{AB}) = \frac{AB}{AD}$ Length probability ratio

$= \frac{8}{16}$ $AB = 8$ and $AD = 8 + 2 + 6 = 16$

$= \frac{1}{2}$, 0.5, or 50%   Simplify.

Exercises

Point M is chosen at random on $\overline{ZP}$. Find the probability of each event.

1. $P(M$ is on $\overline{ZQ}$) $\frac{1}{5}$, 0.2, or 20%

2. $P(M$ is on $\overline{QR}$) $\frac{3}{10}$, 0.3, or 30%

3. $P(M$ is on $\overline{RP}$) $\frac{1}{2}$, 0.5, or 50%

4. $P(M$ is on $\overline{QP}$) $\frac{4}{5}$, 0.8 or 80%

5. **TRAFFIC LIGHT** In a 5-minute traffic cycle, a traffic light is green for 2 minutes 27 seconds, yellow for 6 seconds, and red for 2 minutes 27 seconds. What is the probability that when you get to the light it is green? $\frac{49}{100}$, 0.49, or 49%

6. **GASOLINE** Your mom's mini van has a 24 gallon tank. What is the probability that, when the engine is turned on, the needle on the gas gauge is pointing between $\frac{1}{4}$ and $\frac{1}{2}$ full? $\frac{1}{4}$, 0.25, or 25%

Chapter 13   17   *Glencoe Geometry*

13-3 Skills Practice

Geometric Probability

NAME _____ DATE _____ PERIOD _____

Point X is chosen at random on $\overline{LP}$. Find the probability of each event.

L M   N   O   P
2   8   10   4

1. $P(X \text{ is on } \overline{LN})$ $\frac{5}{12} = 0.41\overline{6} \approx 42\%$

2. $P(X \text{ is on } \overline{MO})$ $\frac{3}{4}$, 0.75, 75%

Find the probability that a point chosen at random lies in the shaded region.

3.
$\frac{1}{3} = 0.\overline{3}$ or about 33%

4.
2
$\frac{\pi}{4} \approx 0.79$ or about 79%

5.
5   12   5
$\frac{5}{17} \approx 0.29$ or about 29%

6. **DESKWORK** The diagram shows the top of a student's desk at home. A dart is dropped on the desk. What is the probability that the dart lands on the book report?
≈ 0.054 or about 5.4%

7. **FROGS** Three frogs are sitting on a 15-foot log. The first two are spaced 5 feet apart and the third frog is 10 feet away from the second one. What is the probability that when a fourth frog hops onto the log it lands between the first two?
$\frac{1}{3} = 0.\overline{3}$ or about 33%

8. **RADIO CONTEST** A radio station is running a contest in which listeners call in when they hear a certain song. The song is 2 minutes 40 seconds long. The radio station promised to play it sometime between noon and 4 P.M. If you tune in to that radio station during that time period, what is the probability the song is playing?
$\frac{1}{90} = 0.0\overline{1} \approx 1\%$

Use the spinner to find each probability. If the spinner lands on a line it is spun again.

9. $P(\text{pointer landing on yellow})$ 30.6%

10. $P(\text{pointer landing on orange})$ 19.4%

Chapter 13   19   Glencoe Geometry

13-3 Study Guide and Intervention (continued)

Geometric Probability

NAME _____ DATE _____ PERIOD _____

Probability with Area Geometric probabilities can also involve area. When determining geometric probability with targets, assume that the object lands within the target area and that it is equally likely that the object will land anywhere in the region.

Example Suppose a coin is flipped into a reflection pond designed with colored tiles that form 3 concentric circles on the bottom. The diameter of the center circle is 4 feet and the circles are spaced 2 feet apart. What is the probability the coin lands in the center?

$P(\text{coin lands in center}) = \dfrac{\text{area of center circle}}{\text{area of base of pond}}$

$= \dfrac{4\pi}{36\pi}$

$= \dfrac{1}{9}$; about 0.11, or 11%

Exercises

1. **LANDING** A parachutist needs to land in the center of a target on a rectangular field that is 120 yards by 30 yards. The target is a circular design with a 10 yard radius. What is the probability the parachutist lands somewhere in the target?
$\frac{\pi}{36} \approx 0.09$ or about 9%

2. **CLOCKS** Jonus watches the second hand on an analog clock as it moves past the numbers. What is the probability that at any given time the second hand on a clock is between the 2- and the 3-hour numbers?
$\frac{1}{12}$, 0.08$\overline{3}$, or about 8%

Find the probability that a point chosen at random lies in the shaded region.

3.
$\frac{2}{3}$, 0.$\overline{6}$, or about 67%

4.
2
$\frac{\pi - 2}{\pi} \approx 0.36$, or about 36%

5.
3   4   3
5
$\frac{4}{7} \approx 0.57$ or about 57%

Use the spinner to find each probability. If the spinner lands on a line it is spun again.

6. $P(\text{pointer landing on red})$
$\frac{1}{9} = 0.\overline{1}$ or about 11%

7. $P(\text{pointer landing on blue})$
$\frac{1}{12} = 0.08\overline{3}$ or about 8%

8. $P(\text{pointer landing on green})$
$\frac{2}{9} = 0.\overline{2}$ or about 22%

Chapter 13   18   Glencoe Geometry

NAME _____ DATE _____ PERIOD _____

13-3 Practice

Geometric Probability

Point L is chosen at random on $\overline{RS}$. Find the probability of each event.

1. $P(L$ is on $\overline{TV})$ $\frac{7}{9}$, $0.\overline{7}$, or about 78%

2. $P(L$ is on $\overline{US})$ $\frac{11}{18}$, $0.6\overline{1}$ or about 61%

Find the probability that a point chosen at random lies in the shaded region.

3.

4.

5.

$\frac{1}{3}$, $0.\overline{3}$, or about 33% $\frac{4-\pi}{4} \approx 0.21$ or about 21% $\frac{\sqrt{3}}{2\pi} \approx 0.28$ or about 28%

Use the spinner to find each probability. If the spinner lands on a line it is spun again.

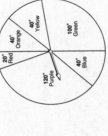

6. P(pointer landing on purple) $\frac{1}{3}$, $0.\overline{3}$, or about 33%

7. P(pointer landing on red) $\frac{1}{18}$, $0.0\overline{5}$, or about 6%

8. PIGS Four pigs are lined up at the feeding trough as shown in the picture. What is the probability that when a fifth pig comes to eat it lines up between the second and third pig?
0.5, 50%

9. MUSIC A certain company plays Mozart's *Eine Kleine Nachtmusik* when its customers are on hold on the telephone. If the length of the complete recording is 2 hours long, what is the probability a customer put on hold will hear the Allegro movement which is 6 minutes, 31 seconds long? **approx. 0.054, or about 5%**

Chapter 13   20   *Glencoe Geometry*

NAME _____ DATE _____ PERIOD _____

13-3 Word Problem Practice

Geometric Probability

1. DARTS A dart is thrown at the dartboard shown. Each sector has the same central angle. The dart has equal probability of hitting any point on the dartboard. What is the probability that the dart will land in a shaded sector?
$\frac{1}{3}$, $0.\overline{3}$, or about 33%

2. SPINNERS Jamie, Joe, and Pat celebrate the end of each work week by ordering spring rolls from a Chinese restaurant. The order comes with 4 spring rolls so somebody gets an extra roll. Because Jamie works full time and Joe and Pat work half time, they decide who gets the extra roll by using a spinner that has a 50% chance of coming up Jamie, and 25% chances of coming up either Joe or Pat. Design such a spinner.
Sample answer:

3. RAIN A container has a square top with a hole as shown. What is the probability that a raindrop that hits the container falls into the hole? Round your answer to the nearest thousandth.
$\frac{\pi}{16} \approx 0.19$ or about 19.63%

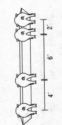

4. ELECTRON MICROSCOPES Crystal places a 7 millimeter by 10 millimeter rectangular plate into the sample chamber of an electron microscope. A black and white checkerboard pattern of 1-millimeter squares was painted over the plate to identify different treatments of the material. When she turns on the monitor, she has no idea at what point on the plate she is looking because the white and black contrast does not show up on the screen. If there are 2 more black squares than white squares, what is the probability that she is looking at a white square?
$\frac{17}{35} \approx 0.49$, or about 49%

5. ENTERTAINMENT A rectangular dance stage is lit by two lights that light up circular regions of the stage. The circles have radii of the same length and each circle passes through the center of the other. The stage perfectly circumscribes the two circles. A spectator throws a bouquet of flowers onto the stage. Assume the bouquet has an equal chance of landing anywhere on the stage. (*Hint:* Use inscribed equilateral triangles.)

a. What is the probability that the flowers land on a lit part of the stage?
0.842

b. What is the probability that the flowers land on the part of the stage where the spotlights overlap?
0.205

Chapter 13   21   *Glencoe Geometry*

Answers

13-3 Spreadsheet Activity

Geometric Probability

You can use a spreadsheet to determine geometric probability.

Example Use a spreadsheet to find the probability of a parachutist landing in the center of this landing pad made up concentric circles.

Step 1 Enter the value of the radius of the center circle in cell A1 and the value of the radius of the whole circle in cell B1.

Step 2 In cell C1 enter an equals sign followed by 3.14*(A1^2). Then press enter. In cell D1 Enter an equals sign followed by 3.14*(B1^2). Then press enter.

Step 3 In cell E1 enter an equals sign followed by C1/D1. Then press Enter. This is the geometric probability of a parachutist landing in the center of the concentric circles.

The probability of a parachutist landing in the center of the landing pad is 0.11.

Exercises

Use a spreadsheet to find the probability of each situation.

1. Refer to Example 1. Find the probability if the radius of the center circle is 4 yards.
0.25

2. What is the probability that an object thrown into the backyard will land in the pool?
0.3

3. Refer to Exercise 2. Suppose the size of the yard remained the same, but the pool was circular with a diameter of 40 feet. What is the new probability that an object thrown into the backyard will land in the pool? **0.16**

4. Find the probability of a care package dropped from an airplane landing on the warehouse in this field.
0.11

5. Refer to Exercise 3. Find the probability the care package lands somewhere in the field rather than on the warehouse.
0.89

Chapter 13   23   Glencoe Geometry

13-3 Enrichment

Polygon Probability

Each problem on this page involves one or more regular polygons. To find the probability of a point chosen at random being in the shaded region, you need to find the ratio of the shaded area to the total area. If you wish, you may substitute numbers for the variables.

Find the probability that a point chosen at random in each figure is in the shaded region. Assume polygons that appear to be regular are regular. Round your answer to the nearest hundredth.

1. $\frac{1}{5}$, 0.20 or 20%

2. $\frac{1}{24}$, ≈ 0.04, or about 4%

3. $\frac{1}{2 + 2\sqrt{2}}$, ≈ 0.21, or about 21%

4. $\frac{\sqrt{3}}{16 + 4\sqrt{3}}$, ≈ 0.08, or about 8%

5. $\frac{\sqrt{3}}{2 + \sqrt{3}}$, ≈ 0.46, or about 46%

6. $\frac{\sqrt{3}}{\sqrt{3} + 1}$, ≈ 0.63, or about 63%

Chapter 13   22   Glencoe Geometry

NAME _____ DATE _____ PERIOD _____

13-4 Study Guide and Intervention (continued)

Simulations

Summarize Data from a Simulation After a simulation is created, the results must be reported with numerical and graphical displays of the data. Compare theoretical and experimental probabilities or expected and average values depending on the type of simulation you run.

Example In a carnival game, a ball is rolled up an incline toward circular regions with different point values. The center circle has a diameter of 6 inches and each successive circle has a radius 4 inches greater than the previous circle.

Let the random variable X represent the point value assigned to a region on the game. The expected value $E(X)$ is found by adding the products of each region's point value and the geometric probability of landing in that region.

$$E(X) = 100 \cdot \frac{72}{121} + 200 \cdot \frac{40}{121} + 300 \cdot \frac{9}{121} \approx 148$$

The frequency table shows the result of the simulation after using a graphing calculator to generate 50 trials. Use these numbers to construct a bar graph and to calculate average value.

Outcome	Frequency
Region 100	19
Region 200	16
Region 300	15
Total	50

Average value $= 100 \cdot \frac{19}{50} + 200 \cdot \frac{16}{50} + 300 \cdot \frac{15}{50} = 192$

The average value is higher than the expected value.

Exercises

1. BASEBALL For a particular baseball player, out of the total number of times he reaches base he gets a walk 6% of the time, a single 55% of the time, a double 30% of the time, a triple 1% of the time, and a home run 8% of the time. The frequency table shows the results of a simulation. Construct a bar graph and compare the experimental probabilities with the theoretical probabilities.

Outcome	Frequency
Walk	5
Single	60
Double	25
Triple	0
Home run	10
Total	100

$P(\text{walk}) = 5\%$, $P(\text{single}) = 60\%$, $P(\text{double}) = 25\%$, $P(\text{triple}) = 0$, $P(\text{home run}) = 10\%$; the singles and home runs were greater than predicted, the walks, doubles, and triples were less than predicted

2. CARNIVAL In a game similar to the game in the above Example, there are four regions in which the ball can fall. The probability that Jani can get 100 points in a roll is 25%, the probability of 200 points is 50%, of 300 points is 20%, and of 400 points is 5%. Calculate the expected value for each roll. $E(X) = 205$

Chapter 13   25   Glencoe Geometry

NAME _____ DATE _____ PERIOD _____

13-4 Study Guide and Intervention

Simulations

Design a Simulation A probability model is a mathematical model that matches something that happens randomly. A simulation is a way to use the model to recreate a situation to help determine the situation's probability.

To design a simulation:
1. Determine each possible outcome and its theoretical probability.
2. State any assumptions.
3. Describe an appropriate probability model for the situation.
4. Define a trial for the situation and state the number of trials to be conducted.

Example Joni got on base 40% of her times at bat last season. Design a simulation to determine the probability that she will get on base in her next at bat this season.

The possible outcomes are Joni gets on base (40%) and Joni doesn't get on base (60%). Assume that Joni will have 90 at bats this season.

Use a spinner divided into two sectors, one containing 40% of the spinner's area, or a central angle of 144°, and the other 60%, or 216°. A trial, one spin of the spinner, will represent one at bat. A successful trial will be getting on base and a failed trial will be not getting on base. The simulation will contain 90 trials.

Exercises

Design a simulation using a geometric probability model.

1. WRESTLING Carlos is the star of the wrestling team. Carlos pinned 80% of his opponents in wrestling matches last season.

Sample answer: Possible outcomes are: pinning (80%), not pinning (20%). Assume Carlos has 20 matches this season. Make a spinner that has one sector with a central angle of 288° and one sector with an angle of 72°. One spin will represent one match. A successful trial will be a pin. An unsuccessful trial will be a non-pin. The simulation will consist of 20 trials.

2. JEANS A trendy jeans store sells jeans in 4 different styles. Last year 45% of their sales was straight leg jeans, 30% was boot cut jeans, 15% was low rise jeans, and 10% was easy fit.

Sample answer: Possible outcomes are: straight leg (45%), boot cut (30%), low rise (15%), easy fit (10%). Assign the integers 1–20: straight leg 1–9, boot cut 10–15, low-rise 16–18, and easy fit 19–20. A trial will represent a customer's choice. The simulation will consist of 20 trials.

3. MOVIE RENTALS A local video store has 5 videos in its fairytale section. Last month Cinderella was rented 35%, Snow White was rented 30%, Sleeping Beauty was rented 20%, Rumpelstiltskin 10%, and Rapunzel 5%.

Sample answer: Possible outcomes are: Cinderella (35%), Snow White (30%), Sleeping Beauty (20%), Rumpelstiltskin (10%), and Rapunzel (5%). Assign the integers 1–20: Cinderella 1–7, Snow White 8–13, Sleeping Beauty 14–17, Rumpelstiltskin 18–19, and Rapunzel 20. A trial will represent a renter's choice. The simulation will consist of 40 trials.

Chapter 13   24   Glencoe Geometry

Answers

NAME _____ DATE _____ PERIOD _____

13-4 Practice

Simulations

Design and conduct a simulation using a geometric probability model. Then report the results using appropriate numerical and graphical summaries.

1. **TRACK** Sean successfully handed off his baton 95% of the time in the 4 × 4 relay last season.
Sample answer: Use a spinner containing sectors of 342° and 18°. Conduct 20 trials. Probability of a successful hand-off = 0.9 and the probability of an unsuccessful hand-off = 0.1. **see students' bar graphs.**

Outcome	Frequency
Successful	18
Not Successful	2
Total	20

2. **BOARD GAME** A game has 50 cards with 10 each numbered 1 to 5, and a player must draw a 2 or 3 to move out of the "start" position.
Sample answer: Use a spinner with 5 equal sectors numbered 1 to 5. Conduct 20 trials. probability of drawing 1 = 0.1; probability of drawing a 2 = 0.15; probability of drawing a 3, 4, or 5 = 0.25 each. **see students' bar graphs.**

Outcome	Frequency
1	2
2	3
3	5
4	5
5	5
Total	20

Design and conduct a simulation using a random number generator. Then report the results using appropriate numerical and graphical summaries.

3. **REAL ESTATE** A real estate company reviewed last year's purchases to determine trends in sizes of homes purchased. The results are shown in the table.

Homes	Purchase %
2BR	10%
3BR	35%
4BR	30%
5BR	15%
6BR	10%

Sample answer: Assign integers 1–20: 2 BR 1–2, 3 BR 3–9, 4 BR 10–15, 5 BR 16–18, 6 BR 19–20. Conduct 20 trials. Probability of the purchase of a 2 BR = 0.05, of a 3 BR = 0.4, of a 4 BR = 0.35, of a 5 BR = 0.15, and of a 6 BR = 0.05. **see students' bar graphs.**

Outcome	Frequency
2BR	1
3BR	8
4BR	7
5BR	3
6BR	1
Total	20

4. **GRADES** On Jonah's math quizzes last semester he scored an A 80% of the time, a B 15% of the time, and a C 5% of the time.
Sample answer: Assign integers 1–20: A 1–16, B 17–19, and C 20. Conduct 20 trials. Probability of scoring an A = 0.8, B = 0.15, and C = 0.05. **see students' bar graphs.**

Outcome	Frequency
A	16
B	3
C	1
Total	20

NAME _____ DATE _____ PERIOD _____

13-4 Skills Practice

Simulations

Design and conduct a simulation using a geometric probability model. Then report the results using appropriate numerical and graphical summaries.

1. **INTERNET** Cory has an online store and auction site. Last year he sold 85% of his inventory.
Sample answer: Use a spinner that is divided into 2 sectors, one at 85% area or 306°, other at 15% or 54°. Perform 50 trials and record answers in frequency table. The probability of selling inventory is 0.88 and the probability of not selling inventory is 0.12.

Outcomes	Frequency
Sold	44
Not sold	6
Total	50

2. **CANDY** Haley works at a candy store. There are 10 types of bulk candy. Find the probability that one type of candy will be chosen more than once in 10 trials.
Sample answer: Use a spinner that is divided into ten 36° sectors. Do 10 trials and record the results in a frequency table. The probability of choosing candy #1, 5, 6, or 7 is 0.1, the probability of choosing candy #2, 3, or 4 is 0, and the probability of choosing candy 8, 9, or 10 is 0.2.

Outcomes	Frequency
Candy 1	1
Candy 2	0
Candy 3	0
Candy 4	0
Candy 5	1
Candy 6	1
Candy 7	1
Candy 8	2
Candy 9	2
Candy 10	2
Total	10

Design and conduct a simulation using a random number generator. Then report the results using appropriate numerical and graphical summaries.

3. **FOOD** According to a survey by a restaurateur's magazine on favorite types of food, 45% of their readers chose Italian, 25% Mexican, 15% American, 10% French, and 5% Ethnic.
Sample answer: Assign 1–20: Italian = 1–9, Mexican = 10–14, American = 15–17, French = 18–19, and Ethnic = 20. Perform 20 trials and record results in a frequency table. The probability of Italian is 0.35, the probability of Mexican is 0.3, the probability of American is 0.25, the probability of French is 0.1 and the probability of Ethnic is 0. Frequency table and bar graph:

Outcome	Frequency
Italian	7
Mexican	6
American	5
French	2
Ethnic	0
Total	20

NAME _____ DATE _____ PERIOD _____

13-4 Enrichment

Pseudorandom Numbers

A random number generator produces numbers with unpredictable outcomes. The random numbers cannot be reproduced using the same generator. A pseudorandom number generator produces numbers that have properties similar to a set of random numbers. While the numbers are not random, they appear to be random. A pseudorandom number generator is used in such applications as MP3 players and computer software. When *random* is chosen on an MP3 player, the generator pseudorandomly chooses a song number. While it may seem that the order of the songs is random, sometimes you may notice a pattern in the song choices. For this reason, the numbers generated are not truly random numbers.

Suppose you have downloaded music onto your MP3 player. You have 6 favorite artists and 10 songs from each of those artists are in your play list. When it is playing in random mode, your MP3 player is programmed to choose the artist and then the song.

1. Design a simulation using a geometric probability model that would find the probability of any of the 60 songs playing (you may have to use more than one device). **Use a die to simulate the choice of artist, and then use a spinner with 10 spaces, each with a central angle of 36°, to simulate the choice of song by that artist. Perform 60 trials.**

2. Conduct the simulation you designed in Exercise 1.

3. Report the results of the simulation. **Answers will vary. Any song has a theoretical probability of being chosen of about 0.017. Frequency table and bar graph will reflect this.**

Suppose you have only 3 favorite artists, but you have 5 songs from Artist 1, 10 songs from Artist 2, and 15 songs from Artist 3. Design and conduct a simulation using a random number generator to answer the following questions.

4. What is the probability a song by Artist 2 will play? **Sample answer: 0.3**

5. What is the probability a song by Artist 3 will play? **Sample answer: 0.5**

6. Do you expect a song from Artist 3 to be more or less likely to play than a song by Artist 1? Why? **More likely; there are more songs by that artist to choose from.**

NAME _____ DATE _____ PERIOD _____

13-4 Word Problem Practice

Simulations

1. **SIMULATIONS** Marta designed a simulation using a coin and a spinner with six equal sections. What situation could Marta have been given to design this simulation? **Sample answer: Finding the probability of a college and major being chosen from a group of seniors choosing between 2 colleges and 6 different majors**

2. **WEATHER** Isaiah says he can use a coin for his simulation of whether or not it will rain tomorrow because there are only 2 possible outcomes. Manny says the weather man said there is a 70% chance it will rain, so a coin is not a good design. Who is correct? Why? **Sample answer: Manny is right. A coin can only be used if the two possible outcomes have equal probability.**

3. **TRAVEL** According to a survey done by a travel agency, 40% of their cruise clients went to the Bahamas, 25% to Mexico, 20% to Alaska, and 15% to Greece. When Jeremy and Jayme were asked to design a simulation that could be used to estimate the probability of a client going to each of these places, Jeremy designed the spinner below.

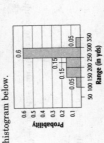

Jayme wants to assign integers to each destination and use the random number generator on her graphing calculator. Which model would allow more trials conducted in a shorter period of time? **Jayme's model**

4. **GOLF** The local driving range advertises that more than 50% of their clients will hit a ball longer than 250 yards at their range. George designed a simulation and then observed for a day at the range. His results are displayed in the histogram below.

Range (in yds): 50 100 150 200 250 300 350

Is the driving range's statement correct? **Yes, each client has more than a 50% chance of hitting a ball further than 250 yards.**

5. **CARNIVAL** A ring toss game awards different point values depending on which dowels rings land. The diagram shows the point values for the different dowels. For this experiment, assume each tossed ring will land on a dowel.

a. Tommy and Catherine calculated the expected value for this experiment as $E(Y) = 36$. Are they correct? **Yes**

b. When Tommy and Catherine conducted the simulation with 50 trials, they found an estimated value of 37.5. Is this reasonable? Why or why not? **Yes. The estimated value is greater than the expected value but close to it. The more trials that are conducted the closer the values will be.**

13-4 Graphing Calculator Activity

Probability Simulation: Conducting a Simulation

Example 1 Use Probability Simulation to simulate choosing a card from a deck of 52 cards.

Step 1 Choose the Probability Simulation Function from the Applications menu. Press ENTER.
- Choose 5. Draw Cards
- Choose Draw from the menu at the bottom of the screen and have the calculator randomly draw cards. A table appears at the right to keep track of the cards drawn.

Step 2 Repeat until 10 cards have been drawn.

Example 2 Design and conduct a simulation using a random number generator.

The school library reviewed the books checked out last month. The results are as follows: 40% fiction, 30% non fiction, 20% biographies, and 10% other.

Step 1 Assign the numbers 1 to 10 to accurately represent the probability data: 1 – 4 = fiction; 5 – 7 = non fiction; 8 – 9 = biographies; 10 = other.

Step 2 Use the calculator. Choose the Probability Simulation Function from the Applications menu. Press ENTER.
- Choose 6. Random Numbers
- Choose SET from the menu at the bottom of the screen. Set the calculator to choose 5 numbers, in the range from 1 – 10, allowing repeats. Press GRAPH to choose OK.

Step 3 Choose DRAW. The calculator will randomly choose 5 numbers and record them in the table. Repeat this 5 times.

Exercises

Design a simulation using the given method. Then use the calculator to conduct the simulation. 1–4: Answers will vary.

Simon made 50% of the goals he attempted in soccer last year.

1. toss coins

2. roll dice

3. pick marbles

4. spin spinner

13-5 Study Guide and Intervention

Probabilities of Independent and Dependent Events

Independent and Dependent Events Compound events, or two or more simple events happening together, can be independent or dependant. Events are **independent events** if the probability of one event does not affect the probability of the other. Events are **dependent events** if one event in some way changes the probability that the other occurs. The following are the **Multiplication Rules for Probability.**

Probability of Two Independent Events	$P(A \text{ and } B) = P(A) \cdot P(B)$
Probability of Two Dependent Events	$P(A \text{ and } B) = P(A) \cdot P(B\|A)$

$P(B\|A)$ is the *conditional probability* and is read *the probability that event B occurs given that event A has already occurred.*

Example The P.E. teacher puts 10 red and 8 blue marbles in a bag. If a student draws a red marble, the student plays basketball. If a student draws a blue marble, the student practices long jump. Suppose Josh draws a marble, and not liking the outcome, he puts it back and draws a second time. What is the probability that on each draw his marble is blue?

Let B represent a blue marble.

$P(B \text{ and } B) = P(B) \cdot P(B)$ Probability of independent events

$P(B) = \frac{4}{9}$ $P(B) = \frac{4}{9}$

$= \frac{4}{9} \cdot \frac{4}{9}$ or $\frac{16}{81}$

So, the probability of Josh drawing two blue marbles is $\frac{16}{81}$ or about 20%.

Exercises

Determine whether the events are *independent* or *dependent.* Then find the probability.

1. A king is drawn from a deck of 52 cards, then a coin is tossed and lands heads up.
independent, $\frac{1}{26}$

2. A spinner with 4 equally spaced sections numbered 1 through 4 is spun and lands on 1, then a die is tossed and rolls a 1.
independent, $\frac{1}{24}$

3. A red marble is drawn from a bag of 2 blue and 5 red marbles and not replaced, then a second red marble is drawn.
dependent, $\frac{10}{21}$

4. A red marble is drawn from a bag of 2 blue and 5 red marbles and then replaced, then a red marble is drawn again.
independent, $\frac{25}{49}$

NAME _____ DATE _____ PERIOD _____

13-5 Skills Practice

Probabilities of Independent and Dependent Events

Determine whether the events are *independent* or *dependent*. Then find the probability.

1. In a game two dice are tossed and both roll a six.

independent; $\frac{1}{36}$

2. From a standard deck of 52 cards, a king is drawn without replacement. Then a second king is drawn.

dependent; $\frac{1}{221}$

3. From a drawer of 8 blue socks and 6 black socks, a blue sock is drawn and not replaced. Then another blue sock is drawn.

dependent; $\frac{4}{13}$

Find each probability.

4. A green marble is selected at random from a bag of 4 yellow, 3 green, and 9 blue marbles and not replaced. What is the probability a second marble selected will be green?

$\frac{2}{15}$

5. A die is tossed. If the number rolled is between 2 and 5, inclusive, what is the probability the number rolled is 4?

$\frac{1}{4}$

6. A spinner with the 7 colors of the rainbow is spun. Find the probability that the color spun is blue, given the color is one of the three primary colors.

$\frac{1}{3}$

7. **VENDING** Mina wants to buy a drink from a vending machine. In her pocket are 2 nickels, 3 quarters and 5 dimes. What is the probability she first pulls out a quarter and then another quarter?

$\frac{1}{15}$

8. **ESSAYS** Jeremy's English class is drawing randomly for people to critique their essays. Jeremy draws first and his friend, Brandon, draws second. If there are 20 people in their class, what is the probability they will draw each other's names?

$\frac{1}{380}$

NAME _____ DATE _____ PERIOD _____

13-5 Study Guide and Intervention (continued)

Probabilities of Independent and Dependent Events

Conditional Probabilities Conditional probability is used to find the probability of dependent events. It also can be used when additional information is known about an event.

The conditional probability of B given A is $P(B|A) = \dfrac{P(A \text{ and } B)}{P(A)}$ where $P(A) \neq 0$.

Example The Spanish Club is having a Cinco de Mayo fiesta. The 10 students randomly draw cards numbered with consecutive integers from 1 to 10. Students who draw odd numbers will bring main dishes. Students who draw even numbers will bring desserts. If Cynthia is bringing a dessert, what is the probability that she drew the number 10?

Since Cynthia is bringing dessert, she must have drawn an even number.

Let A be the event that an even number is drawn.

Let B be the event that the number 10 is drawn.

$P(B|A) = \dfrac{P(A \text{ and } B)}{P(A)}$ Conditional Probability

$\qquad = \dfrac{0.5 \cdot 0.1}{0.5}$ $P(A) = \dfrac{1}{2} = 0.5$ and $P(B) = \dfrac{1}{10} = 0.1$

$\qquad = 0.1$ Simplify.

The probability Cynthia drew the number 10 is 0.1 or 10%.

Exercises

1. A blue marble is selected at random from a bag of 3 red and 9 blue marbles and not replaced. What is the probability that a second marble selected will be blue?

$\frac{8}{11}$

2. A die is rolled. If the number rolled is less than 5, what is the probability that it is the number 2?

$\frac{1}{4}$

3. A quadrilateral has a perimeter of 16 and all side lengths are even integers. What is the probability that the quadrilateral is a square?

$\frac{1}{4}$

4. A spinner with 8 evenly sized sections and numbered 1 through 8 is spun. Find the probability that the number spun is 6 given that it is an even number.

$\frac{1}{4}$

Answers

NAME _____ DATE _____ PERIOD _____

13-5 Word Problem Practice

Probabilities of Independent and Dependent Events

1. DRIVING The probability that a person has received a speeding ticket is 0.35. The probability of a person driving a red car is 0.15. What is the probability of randomly choosing a driver with a speeding ticket whose car is not red?
0.2975

2. GAMES In a game, the spinner with 4 spaces numbered 1 to 4 is spun and a die is rolled.

What is the probability of spinning an even number on the spinner and rolling an even number on the die?
$\frac{1}{4}$

3. CARDS Three cards are drawn and not replaced from a standard deck. What is the probability that all three cards will be from different suits?

0.398

4. HEALTH Jane conducted a survey at her school and found that the probability of a student contracting a version of the flu last year at her school was 5%. She also found the probability of a student contracting the stomach flu at her school last year was 1%. What is the probability that if a person develops the flu, it will be the stomach flu?
20%

5. BIRTHDAYS Since there are 365 days in a year, the probability of a person's birthday on any random day is about 0.00274.

APRIL 2008						
Sunday	Monday	Tuesday	Wednesday	Thursday	Friday	Saturday
		1	2	3	4	5
6	7	8	9	10	11	12
13	14	15	16	17	18	19
20	21	22	23	24	25	26
27	28	29	30			

a. What is the probability that two people will have the same birthday?
0.00273

b. What is the probability that out of thirty people, two will have the same birthday?
0.706

Chapter 13   35   *Glencoe Geometry*

NAME _____ DATE _____ PERIOD _____

13-5 Practice

Probabilities of Independent and Dependent Events

Determine whether the events are *independent* or *dependent.* Then find the probability.

1. From a bag of 5 red and 6 green marbles, a red marble is drawn and not replaced. Then a green marble is drawn.
dependent, $\frac{3}{11}$

2. In a game, you roll an odd number on a die and then spin a spinner with 6 evenly sized spaces numbered 1 to 6 and get an even number.
independent, $\frac{1}{4}$

3. A card is randomly chosen from a standard deck of 52 cards then replaced, and a second card is then chosen. What is the probability that the first card is the ace of hearts and the second card is the ace of diamonds?
independent, $\frac{1}{2704}$

Find each probability.

4. A die is tossed. If the number rolled is greater than 2, what is the probability that the number rolled is 3?
$\frac{1}{4}$

5. A black shoe is selected at random from a bin of 6 black shoes and 4 brown shoes and not replaced. What is the probability that a second shoe selected will be black?
$\frac{5}{9}$

6. A spinner with 12 evenly sized sections and numbered 1 to 12 is spun. What is the probability that the number spun is 12 given that the number is even?
$\frac{1}{6}$

7. GAME In a game, a spinner with 8 equally sized sections numbered 1 to 8 is spun and a die is tossed. What is the probability of landing on an odd number on the spinner and rolling an even number on the die?
$\frac{1}{4}$

8. APPROVAL A survey found that 8 out of 10 parents approved of the new principal's performance. If 4 parents' names are chosen, with replacement, what is the probability they all approve of the principal's performance?
$\frac{256}{625}$ **or about 41%**

Chapter 13   34   *Glencoe Geometry*

13-5 Enrichment

NAME _____ DATE _____ PERIOD _____

Weather Forecasting

When you watch the news the weather person might say, "there will be a 60% chance of rain tomorrow." This means that $P(\text{rain tomorrow}) = \frac{60}{100}$. Notice that this also says that $P(\text{no rain tomorrow}) = \frac{40}{100}$.

But rain tomorrow is dependent upon a number of factors; such as if it rains today, if clouds form over the night, or if it rained today in a city to the east.

Weather forecasts are predictions of what might happen; they are not always correct. They are independent of the weather because their forecast has no effect on the weather.

Day	Conditions	High/Low
Monday	☀ Sunny	70/50
Tuesday	🌧 Rain	68/54
Wednesday	⛅ Partly Cloudy	62/53

Example A forecaster for the *Springfield Times* says there is a 40% chance that it will rain. The forecaster is correct 75% of the time.

a. What is the probability the forecaster will be right and it will rain?

Since these events are independent the probability will be $\frac{40}{100} \cdot \frac{75}{100} = \frac{3000}{10,000}$ or $\frac{3}{10}$.

b. What is the probability that the forecaster will be wrong and it not rain?

The probability that the forecaster will be wrong is 25%, while the probability that it will not rain is 60%. Since these events are independent the probability will be $\frac{25}{100} \cdot \frac{60}{100} = \frac{1500}{10,000}$ or $\frac{15}{100}$.

Exercises

A forecaster for the *Union Herald* says that there is a 40% chance that there is a 60% chance of rain. If the form. They also say that if clouds form there is a 60% chance of rain. If the forecaster is correct 55% of the time, find the following probabilities.

1. clouds will form and it will not rain **0.16**

2. clouds will not form and the forecaster will be right **0.33**

3. clouds will not form and the forecaster will be wrong **0.27**

4. clouds will form, it will rain and the forecaster will be right **0.132**

5. clouds will form, it will rain and the forecaster will be wrong **0.108**

13-6 Study Guide and Intervention

NAME _____ DATE _____ PERIOD _____

Probabilities of Mutually Exclusive Events

Mutually Exclusive Events If two events cannot happen at the same time, and therefore have no common outcomes, they are said to be **mutually exclusive**. The following are the Addition Rules for Probability:

Probability of Mutually Exclusive Events	$P(A \text{ or } B) = P(A) + P(B)$
Probability of Non-Mutually Exclusive Events	$P(A \text{ or } B) = P(A) + P(B) - P(A \text{ and } B)$

Example At the ballpark souvenir shop, there are 15 posters of the first baseman, 20 of the pitcher, 14 of the center fielder, and 12 of the shortstop. What is the probability that a fan choosing a poster at random will choose a poster of the center fielder or the shortstop?

These are mutually exclusive events because the posters are of two different players.

Let C represent selecting a poster of the center fielder.
Let S represent selecting a poster of the shortstop.

$$P(C \text{ or } S) = P(C) + P(S)$$
$$= \frac{14}{61} + \frac{12}{61}$$
$$= \frac{26}{61} \text{ or about } 43\%$$

Exercises

Determine whether the events are *mutually exclusive* or *not mutually exclusive*. Then find the probability. Round to the nearest hundredth.

1. **SHELTER** selecting a cat or dog at the animal shelter that has 15 cats, 25 dogs, 9 rabbits and 3 horses

   mutually exclusive, 0.77

2. **GAME** rolling a 6 or an even number on a die while playing a game

   not mutually exclusive, 0.5

3. **AWARDS** The student of the month gets to choose his or her award from 9 gift certificates to area restaurants, 8 CDs, 6 DVDs, or 5 gift cards to the mall. What is the probability that the student of the month chooses a CD or DVD?

   mutually exclusive, 0.5

4. **STUDENT COUNCIL** According to the table shown at the right, what is the probability that a person on a student council committee is a junior or on the service committee?

   not mutually exclusive, 0.57

Committee	Soph.	Junior	Senior
Service	4	5	6
Advertising	3	2	2
Dances	4	8	6
Administrative Liaison	1	1	4

Answers

NAME _____ DATE _____ PERIOD _____

13-6 Skills Practice

Probabilities of Mutually Exclusive Events

Determine whether the events are *mutually exclusive* or *not mutually exclusive.* Then find the probability. **Round to the nearest tenth of a percent if necessary.**

1. drawing a card from a standard deck and choosing a king or an ace

mutually exclusive; $\frac{2}{13}$ or about 15.4%

2. rolling a pair of dice and doubles or a sum of 6 is rolled

not mutually exclusive; $\frac{5}{18}$ or about 27.8%

3. drawing a two or a heart from a standard deck of 52 cards

not mutually exclusive; $\frac{4}{13}$ or about 30.8%

4. rolling a pair of dice and a sum of 8 or 12 is rolled

mutually exclusive; $\frac{1}{6}$ or about 16.7%

Determine the probability of each event.

5. If the chance of being selected for the student bailiff program is 1 in 200, what is the probability of not being chosen? **$\frac{199}{200}$ or 0.995**

6. If you have a 40% chance of making a free throw, what is the probability of missing a free throw? **60% or 0.6**

7. What is the probability of spinning a spinner numbered 1 to 6 and not landing on 5? **$\frac{5}{6}$ or about 0.83**

8. Jeanie bought 10 raffle tickets. If 250 were sold, what is the probability that one of Jeanie's tickets will not be selected? **$\frac{240}{250}$ or 0.96**

Chapter 13   39   *Glencoe Geometry*

NAME _____ DATE _____ PERIOD _____

13-6 Study Guide and Intervention (continued)

Probabilities of Mutually Exclusive Events

Probabilities of Complements The complement of an event A is all of the outcomes in the sample space that are not included as outcomes of event A.

Probability of the Complement of an Event	$P(\text{not } A) = 1 - P(A)$

Example A school has a photography display of 100 pictures. One of the pictures will be chosen for display at the district office. Lorenzo has 3 pictures on display. What is the probability that one of his photographs is not chosen?

Let A represent selecting one of Lorenzo's photographs.
Then find the probability of the complement of A.

$P(\text{not } A) = 1 - P(A)$ Probability of a complement

$= 1 - \frac{3}{100}$ Substitution

$= \frac{97}{100}$ or 0.97   Simplify

The probability that one of Lorenzo's photos is not selected is 97%.

Exercises

Determine the probability of each event.

1. If there is a 4 in 5 chance that your mom will tell you to clean your room today after school, what is the probability that she won't? **0.2**

2. What is the probability of drawing a card from a standard deck and not getting a spade? **0.75**

3. What is the probability of flipping a coin and not landing on tails? **0.5**

4. What is the probability of rolling a pair of dice and not rolling a 6? **0.69**

5. A survey found that about 90% of the junior class is right handed. If 2 juniors are chosen at random out of 100 juniors, what is the probability that at least one of them is not right handed? **0.191**

Chapter 13   38   *Glencoe Geometry*

Answers (Lesson 13-6)

NAME _____ DATE _____ PERIOD _____

13-6 Word Problem Practice

Probabilities of Mutually Exclusive Events

1. CHESS A chess board has 64 squares, 32 white and 32 black, and is played with 16 black and 16 white pieces.

If all the pieces are placed randomly on the board, what is the probability of two white knights being on black squares or a black bishop being on a black square?
0.726

2. PARKS The table below shows the Parks and Recreation Department classes and the number of participants aged 7–9.

Age	Swimming	Drama	Art
7	40	35	25
8	30	21	14
9	20	44	11

What is the probability that a participant chosen at random is in Drama or is an 8-year-old?
0.6

3. CARDS What is the probability of pulling two cards from a 52-card deck that are both red or both fours?
0.2488

4. COLLEGE In Evan's senior class of 100 students, 89% are attending in-state colleges. If two people are chosen at random from the entire class, what is the probability that at least one of them is not going to an in-state college?
0.21

5. DESIGN Dennis and Kelly are designing a game for a third grade math class to help students practice their basic facts. They decide that the game will use a pair of dice and the players will have to find the sum of the numbers rolled. Dennis and Kelly created the table below to help determine probabilities.

1, 1	1, 2	1, 3	1, 4	1, 5	1, 6
2, 1	2, 2	2, 3	2, 4	2, 5	2, 6
3, 1	3, 2	3, 3	3, 4	3, 5	3, 6
4, 1	4, 2	4, 3	4, 4	4, 5	4, 6
5, 1	5, 2	5, 3	5, 4	5, 5	5, 6
6, 1	6, 2	6, 3	6, 4	6, 5	6, 6

Each player will roll the pair of dice twice during that player's turn.

a. What is the probability of rolling a pair or two numbers that add to seven?
0.333

b. What is the probability of rolling two numbers that add to an even number or not rolling a 2?
0.8056

NAME _____ DATE _____ PERIOD _____

13-6 Practice

Probabilities of Mutually Exclusive Events

Determine whether the events are *mutually exclusive* or *not mutually exclusive*. Then find the probability. Round to the nearest hundredth.

1. drawing a card from a standard deck and choosing a 7 or a 10
mutually exclusive, 0.15

2. rolling a pair of dice and getting a sum of either 6 or 8
mutually exclusive, 0.28

3. selecting a number from a list of integers 1 to 20 and getting a prime or even number
not mutually exclusive, 0.85

4. drawing a card from a standard deck and getting a queen or a heart
not mutually exclusive, 0.31

Determine the probability of each event. Round to the nearest hundredth.

5. What is the probability of drawing a card from a standard deck and not choosing an ace?
0.92

6. What is the probability of rolling a pair of dice and not rolling the same number?
0.83

7. If the chance of being chosen for the principal's task force is 3 in 20, what is the probability of not being chosen?
0.85

8. What is the probability of spinning a spinner numbered from 1 to 12 and not landing on 6?
0.92

9. TRAFFIC If the chance of making a green light at a certain intersection is 35%, what is the probability of arriving when the light is yellow or red?
0.65

10. RAFFLE Michael bought 50 raffle tickets. If 1000 were sold, what is the probability that one of Michael's tickets will not win?
0.95

Answers

NAME _____ DATE _____ PERIOD _____

13-6 Enrichment

Demographics

Demographics is the term used to refer to characteristics of the population including age, race, gender, education level, income, employment status, and other variables. Marketing research used by advertisers and polling data used by politicians are two areas in which demographics are an important part of the data. Sometimes the people under consideration fall into more than one category. Sometimes the events being researched are mutually exclusive.

Suppose an exit poll held outside a voting area on the day of an election produced these results. Use the table to answer the questions below.

Age and Gender	Votes for Candidate A	Votes for Candidate B
18–30 Male	19	32
18–30 Female	31	18
31–45 Male	51	12
31–45 Female	43	20
46–60 Male	42	35
46–60 Female	20	42
60+ Male	45	21
60+ Female	27	18

1. Which events are mutually exclusive?
   voting for Candidate A or B

2. Find the probability that a 46–60 year-old male would vote for Candidate A.
   0.55

3. Find the probability that a female would vote for Candidate A.
   0.55

4. Find the probability that someone who voted for Candidate B was female and age 18–30.
   0.09

5. According to the data, on which demographic(s) does Candidate A need to focus campaign efforts?
   Candidate A needs to focus on 18–30 year-old males and 46–60 year-old females.

6. On which demographic(s) does Candidate B need to focus campaign efforts?
   Candidate B needs to focus on 18–30 year old females, 31–45 year-old males and females, and anyone over 60.

Chapter 13   42   Glencoe Geometry

Chapter 13 Assessment Answer Key

Quiz 1 (Lessons 13-1 and 13-2)
Page 45

1. **H-E, H-C, J-E, J-C**

2.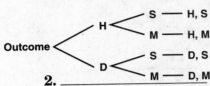

3. **72**

4. $\dfrac{1}{105}$

5. $\dfrac{1}{600}$

Quiz 2 (Lesson 13-3)
Page 45

1. $\dfrac{1}{3}$

2. $\dfrac{2}{3}$

3. **0.28**

4. **0.11**

5. **0.32**

Quiz 3 (Lesson 13-4)
Page 46

1.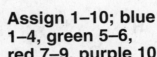
   spinner with 2 regions, one central angle 216°, and one 144°

Assign 1–10; blue 1–4, green 5–6, red 7–9, purple 10.

2.

3. $\dfrac{1}{12}$

4. $\dfrac{1}{169}$

5. $\dfrac{4}{663}$

Quiz 4 (Lesson 13-5)
Page 46

1. $\dfrac{2}{13}$

2. $\dfrac{5}{18}$

3. $\dfrac{1}{6}$

4. **20%**

5. $\dfrac{5}{6}$

Mid-Chapter Test
Page 47

Part I

1. **C**

2. **H**

3. **D**

4. **F**

5. **A**

Part II

6. **EJ, ES, SJ, SS**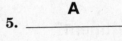

7.

8. $\dfrac{1}{5040}$

9. $\dfrac{1}{2450}$

10. $\dfrac{1}{20,160}$

Answers

Chapter 13 Assessment Answer Key

Vocabulary Test
Page 48

Form 1
Page 49

Page 50

1. true

2. true

3. false; product

4. true

5. experiment

6. factorial

7. probability model

8. dependent events

9. Sample Answer: a method to graphically find all of the possible outcomes of an event

10. Sample answer: a formula used to find all of the possible outcomes of an event

1. D

2. H

3. B

4. F

5. A

6. G

7. D

8. G

9. B

10. G

11. C

12. F

13. B

14. G

15. D

16. F

17. D

18. G

B: $\dfrac{1}{5}$

Chapter 13 Assessment Answer Key

Form 2A
Page 51

Page 52

Form 2B
Page 53

Page 54

1. ___**B**___

2. ___**J**___

3. ___**B**___

4. ___**H**___

5. ___**C**___

6. ___**G**___

7. ___**D**___

8. ___**F**___

9. ___**C**___

10. ___**F**___

11. ___**C**___

12. ___**G**___

13. ___**D**___

14. ___**J**___

15. ___**B**___

16. ___**H**___

17. ___**C**___

18. ___**G**___

B: ___$\frac{5}{6}$, about, 0.83, or 83%___

1. ___**C**___

2. ___**J**___

3. ___**A**___

4. ___**H**___

5. ___**B**___

6. ___**F**___

7. ___**C**___

8. ___**F**___

9. ___**D**___

10. ___**H**___

11. ___**B**___

12. ___**F**___

13. ___**C**___

14. ___**H**___

15. ___**A**___

16. ___**J**___

17. ___**B**___

18. ___**G**___

B: ___$\frac{4 - \pi}{4}$___

Answers

Chapter 13 Assessment Answer Key

Form 2C

Page 55

1.
```
1,1  2,1  3,1  4,1
1,2  2,2  3,2  4,2
1,3  2,3  3,3  4,3
1,4  2,4  3,4  4,4
```

2. **1296**

3. **150**

4. $\frac{1}{20}$, 0.05, or 5%

5. $\frac{1}{120}$, 0.0083, or 0.83%

6. $\frac{1}{19,958,400}$

7. $\frac{1}{120}$, 0.0083, or 0.83%

8. $\frac{10}{12}$, 0.83, or 0.83%

9. $\frac{3}{4}$, 0.75, or 75%

10. $\frac{17}{72}$, 0.24, or 24%

Page 56

11. Sample answer: red: 0, 1; blue 2, 3, 4; green 5; yellow 6; orange, 7, 8, 9

12. $\frac{1}{55}$, 0.018, or 1.8%

13. a central angle of about 79°

14. $\frac{4}{663}$, 0.006 or 0.6%

15. $\frac{1}{36}$, 0.028 or 2.8%

16. $\frac{4}{13}$, 0.31, or 31%

17. **155.56**

18. $\frac{5}{9}$, 0.56, or 56%

19. $\frac{25}{36}$

20. $\frac{9}{1250}$, 0.9928, or 99.28%

B. $\frac{4 - \pi}{4}$

Chapter 13 Assessment Answer Key

Form 2D
Page 57

1. R-R, R-B, R-Y, R-G, B-R, B-B, B-Y, B-G, Y-R, Y-B, Y-Y, Y-G, G-R, G-B, G-Y, G-G

2. 216

3. 90

4. $\frac{1}{12}$

5. $\frac{1}{120}$

6. $\frac{1}{453,600}$

7. $\frac{1}{120}$

8. $\frac{1}{4}$, 0.25, or 25%

9. $\frac{1}{6}$, 0.17, or 17%

10. $\frac{29}{60}$ or 0.48

11. $\frac{1}{3}$, 0.33, or 33%

Page 58

12. sample answer: a spinner with sectors 162° and 198°

13. $\frac{13}{20}$, 0.65, or 65%

14. a central angle of about 234°

15. $\frac{1}{17}$, 0.06, or 6%

16. $\frac{1}{36}$, 0.027, or 2.7%

17. $\frac{4}{13}$, 0.31, or 31%

18. $\frac{10}{13}$, 0.77, or 77%

19. 155.6

20. 0.21

B: $\frac{1}{50}$, 0.02, or 2%

Copyright © Glencoe/McGraw-Hill, a division of The McGraw-Hill Companies, Inc.

A25

Glencoe Geometry

Chapter 13 Assessment Answer Key

Form 3
Page 59

1. BB, BT, TB, TT

2. 36

3. 18

4. $\frac{1}{10}$, 0.1, or 10%

5. $\frac{1}{5}$

6. $\frac{1}{360}$

7. $\frac{1}{15}$

8. <

9. $\frac{9}{20}$, 0.45, or 45%

10. $\frac{13}{36}$, 0.36, or 36%

Page 60

11. $\frac{1}{2}$

12. Sample answer: flip a coin

13. experimental probability

14. false

15. 166.7

16. $\frac{13}{204}$, 0.06, or 6%

17. $\frac{5}{36}$, 0.14, or 14%

18. $\frac{1}{2}$, 0.5, or 50%

19. $\frac{10}{13}$, 0.77, or 77%

20. $\frac{112}{275}$, 0.41 or 41%

B: sometimes

Chapter 13 Assessment Answer Key

Extended-Response Test, Page 61
Scoring Rubric

Score	General Description	Specific Criteria
4	**Superior** A correct solution that is supported by well-developed, accurate explanations	• Shows thorough understanding of the concepts of *finding sample spaces, probability, independent and dependent events, and geometric probability.* • Uses appropriate strategies to solve problems. • Computations are correct. • Written explanations are exemplary. • Figures and graphs are accurate and appropriate. • Goes beyond requirements of some or all problems.
3	**Satisfactory** A generally correct solution, but may contain minor flaws in reasoning or computation	• Shows an understanding of the concepts of *congruent finding sample spaces, probability, independent and dependent events, and geometric probability.* • Uses appropriate strategies to solve problems. • Computations are mostly correct. • Written explanations are effective. • Figures and graphs are mostly accurate and appropriate. • Satisfies all requirements of problems.
2	**Nearly Satisfactory** A partially correct interpretation and/or solution to the problem	• Shows an understanding of most of the concepts of *finding sample spaces, probability, independent and dependent events, and geometric probability.* • May not use appropriate strategies to solve problems. • Computations are mostly correct. • Written explanations are satisfactory. • Figures and graphs are mostly accurate. • Satisfies the requirements of most of the problems.
1	**Nearly Unsatisfactory** A correct solution with no supporting evidence or explanation	• Final computation is correct. • No written explanations or work shown to substantiate the final computation. • Figures and graphs may be accurate but lack detail or explanation. • Satisfies minimal requirements of some of the problems.
0	**Unsatisfactory** An incorrect solution indicating no mathematical understanding of the concept or task, or no solution is given	• Shows little or no understanding of most of the concepts of *finding sample spaces, probability, independent and dependent events, and geometric probability.* • Does not use appropriate strategies to solve problems. • Computations are incorrect. • Written explanations are unsatisfactory. • Figures and graphs are inaccurate or inappropriate. • Does not satisfy requirements of problems. • No answer given.

Answers

In addition to the scoring rubric found on page A27, the following sample answers may be used as guidance in evaluating open-ended assessment items.

1a.

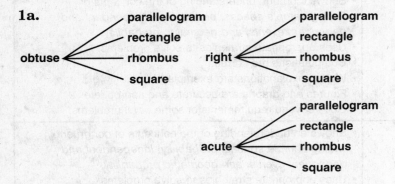

1b. Choosing an acute triangle or a square are not mutually exclusive events. Therefore the probability would be $\frac{4}{12} + \frac{3}{12} - \frac{1}{12} = \frac{1}{2}$ or 50%.

2a. Sample answer: Independent events are events where the outcome of the first event does not affect the outcome of the second event. Choosing a card, replacing it, and then choosing a second card is an example of independent events.

2b. Sample answer: Dependent events are events where the outcome of the first event affects the outcome of the second event. Choosing a card, not replacing it, and then choosing a second card is an example of dependent events.

3a. The area of the segment is $\frac{50}{360} \cdot \pi\, 5^2 - \frac{1}{2}(10 \sin 25°)(5 \cos 25°) \approx 1.3$ cm². The probability that a point chosen at random lies in the shaded region is $\frac{\text{area of the segment}}{\text{area of the circle}}$.

3b. 0.02

Chapter 13 Assessment Answer Key

Standardized Test Practice
Page 62

1. Ⓐ Ⓑ Ⓒ ●

2. ● Ⓖ Ⓗ Ⓙ

3. Ⓐ Ⓑ ● Ⓓ

4. Ⓕ Ⓖ ● Ⓙ

5. ● Ⓑ Ⓒ Ⓓ

6. Ⓕ ● Ⓗ Ⓙ

7. Ⓐ Ⓑ ● Ⓓ

8. Ⓕ ● Ⓗ Ⓙ

Page 63

9. ● Ⓑ Ⓒ Ⓓ

10. Ⓕ Ⓖ Ⓗ ●

11. Ⓐ Ⓑ ● Ⓓ

12. Ⓕ Ⓖ ● Ⓙ

13. Ⓐ Ⓑ ● Ⓓ

14. ● Ⓖ Ⓗ Ⓙ

15. 5

16. 3

Answers

Chapter 13 Assessment Answer Key

17. _____ 12 _____

18. _____ 10.25 _____

19. _____ 126 m² _____

20. _____ 175.9 in² _____

21. _____ 1526.8 ft³ _____

22. _____ (0.5, 5.5) _____

23a. _____ 721.73 cm² _____

  b. _____ 1587.9 cm³ _____

  c. _____ 5359.3 cm³ _____

Chapter 13 Assessment Answer Key

Unit 4 Test
Page 65

Page 66

1. $m\angle NJK = 72$; length of $\overset{\frown}{NK}$ is about 17.59 cm.

2. $LK = 16$, $MK = 32$, and $m\overset{\frown}{MNK} = 106.2$

3. $324\pi - 486\sqrt{3}$ or about 176.1 in^2

4. 33 units^2

5. $\dfrac{44}{100}$, 0.44, or 44%

6. triangular prism; bases: $\triangle ABC$ and $\triangle DEF$

7. 1009.4 units^2

8. $\dfrac{4}{13}$

9. 129.8 in^2

10. 8.5 m

11. 127.5 ft^2

12. 181.2 in^2

13. 2035.8 cm^2

14. 102.4 ft^3

15. 1900.7 in^3

16. cylinder

17. similar

18. Sample answer: spin a spinner 20 times with one sector 144° and the other sector 216°.

Answers